Penguin Health
Coping with Young Child

Jo Douglas read Psychology at Bristol University and after taking a postgraduate certificate in the teaching of infants and primary-school children, she gained her M.Sc. in Clinical Psychology at the University of Birmingham in 1975. She joined the Hospital for Sick Children, Great Ormond Street, in 1975 where she worked a joint appointment and is now the Principal Clinical Psychologist. She has had a wide clinical experience with children and families and now works in the Day Centre for pre-school children and parents. Children with a variety of emotional and behavioural difficulties attend with their parents for advice on management. She has specialized in behavioural work with families and has written extensively for professionals as well as for parents. She has two young children, Alexandra and Amanda, who have demonstrated the pleasure and the stresses of being a parent with young children.

Naomi Richman is Reader at the Institute of Child Health, London, and Honorary Consultant Psychiatrist at the Hospital for Sick Children, Great Ormond Street. She completed her medical training at St Hilda's College, Oxford, and at the Middlesex Hospital, London, and then went on to train in psychiatry at the Maudsley Hospital and in epidemiology at Columbia University, New York. She is medical director of a pre-school day centre for children with developmental and behavioural difficulties and is particularly concerned about the problems faced by families with young children. Dr Richman has carried out a number of surveys looking at the behaviour of young children, including one on sleeping patterns. She is currently involved in research projects looking at ways of preventing sleep difficulties and of helping parents whose children are not sleeping well. Other research intrerests include the role of day nurseries and nursery schools in children's lives and the adjustment of girls in later adolescence.

A companion volume, *My Child Won't Sleep*, written by Jo Douglas and Naomi Richman, is also published by Penguin.

Jo Douglas and Naomi Richman

COPING
WITH YOUNG CHILDREN

A handbook of daily management for parents
of young children

Penguin Books

PENGUIN BOOKS

Published by the Penguin Group
27 Wrights Lane, London w8 5tz, England
Viking Penguin Inc., 40 West 23rd Street, New York, New York 10010, USA
Penguin Books Australia Ltd, Ringwood, Victoria, Australia
Penguin Books Canada Ltd, 2801 John Street, Markham, Ontario, Canada l3r 1b4
Penguin Books (NZ) Ltd, 182–190 Wairau Road, Auckland 10, New Zealand

Penguin Books Ltd, Registered Offices: Harmondsworth, Middlesex, England

First published 1984
Reprinted 1985, 1988

Copyright © Jo Douglas and Naomi Richman, 1984
All rights reserved

Filmset in 9/11 Trump by
Rowland Phototypesetting Ltd,
Bury St Edmunds, Suffolk
Printed and bound in Great Britain by
Cox & Wyman Ltd, Reading

Contents

Chapter 1
Introduction

Early childhood is a time of rapid development and change. There are so many new experiences to face: toilet training, the first separations, birth of a new baby, beginning play group. Just when you have got into a routine you are faced with a new challenge, and you both have to adapt quickly to the next phase.

Not surprisingly this process doesn't always run smoothly, and at times your child's behaviour is a worry. She may suddenly refuse to eat anything but crackers and chips, have a temper every morning whatever clothes you suggest she wears, refuse to stay with someone she used to love being with. At times things are bound to get on top of you and you begin to wonder whether your management of her is completely wrong.

This handbook is an attempt to help you cope with the everyday problems of childhood. Our suggestions are based on our experiences working in a clinic with children who show disturbed or difficult behaviour. We think that our techniques can help parents whose children have less serious problems, and that at times they might also be useful in preventing problems starting in the first place.

There is nothing new or unusual about these suggested methods, and you may find you are using them already. If you are, we hope that this handbook will help you to use them more effectively.

We have included some descriptions of friends' experiences with their children and of children we have met in our clinics. Names and other details have been altered for confidentiality. It can be helpful to know how others have tackled similar problems and to see that your experiences are shared by many other parents.

What is a problem?

It is quite arbitrary whether a particular behaviour is called a 'problem' or not. Some behaviours only turn into a problem as a child gets older. For instance, about a third of all children aged three wet the bed, but at six years old bed-wetting is less common and could be considered a problem. Other behaviours like nail-biting, tempers or fighting over toys occur so commonly that they are accepted as a normal part of growing up. Only you as parents can decide what is a problem for you. You may take most difficulties in your stride but become filled with despair at such things as refusal to use the potty (see Chapter 12).

Problems tend to wax and wane over time, and an isolated difficult behaviour is usually not a sign of emotional upset. But even though a problem will probably clear up in a few months it can be troublesome at the time, and you may be glad to have some extra ideas to fall back on which will ease the situation for you and help your child cope with the inevitable challenges of growing up.

Surveys find that difficult behaviours are extremely common in young children and that certain problems are typical for each age.[1,2] Waking problems are most common in one- to two-year-olds, food fads and poor appetite in two- to three-year olds, and fears and aggressive behaviour in slightly older children. It's not always clear why problems develop when they do. Sometimes they occur as a normal stage in development, such as being clinging around the age of nine months (Chapter 7). Sometimes they are a response to upsetting events like being in hospital; at other times problem behaviours come and go out of the blue for no obvious reason.

Often the difficulties are part of normal childhood development as children learn to cope with their own emotions and the world around them. You don't want to suppress these emotions, but by your responses you help your child to learn how to deal with them and how to handle difficult, frustrating or upsetting situations.

In this book we describe common behaviours that you as

parents are likely to encounter or to worry about. For convenience, the book is divided into chapters, dealing with the various areas of difficulty, such as feeding, toilet training, tempers and so on. A companion book, *My Child Won't Sleep*, discusses sleeping problems and ways of dealing with them.

Throughout all the chapters we try to deal with the following questions which are of concern to parents whatever the age of their child.

What is normal development?

Although the book is not specifically about all aspects of development from birth to five years, we have tried to help you decide whether a particular behaviour shown by your child is 'normal' for her age. Many behaviours worry parents because they are unexpected. They may expect the clinging stage of nine to eighteen months but not know that most one-year-olds enjoy eating soil, or head-banging and rocking, from time to time (see Chapter 6). If you are not prepared for this you may be convinced that there is something wrong with your child. It is common for a child to develop signs of tension or upset such as losing her appetite, starting to soil her pants again, becoming clinging and whiny. Sometimes it is clear why this has happened: there has been a new baby in the family (see Chapter 10), a sudden separation, the child has started nursery school. Sometimes there is no clear cause but the behaviours seem to be part of ordinary development, like the poor appetite, nightmares or increased fears which occur so often around the age of three.

Usually these signs of upset come and go; only if they are prolonged or if there are many difficulties in behaviour is it likely that your child is seriously emotionally disturbed.

How do I cope with the next step in development?

Some stages of development may be particularly difficult for you and your child to get through. You may feel you are never going to get your child on to solids or wean her or perhaps potty train her; the obstacles seem insuperable and you may be surprised at how upset the whole situation makes you feel.

Why do parents have so many doubts about themselves nowadays? Perhaps it is because fashions of child-rearing change so rapidly and advice varies so much. One 'authority' says you should start solids at three months and another says six months. If you listen to all these opinions you can easily become confused and angry.

Mrs Grant, now a grandmother, described how she brought up all her six children differently. One was weaned at six months and another at nine months; one started solids at three months and another at seven months, and so on. By the time she reached her fifth child she decided that perhaps the experts she had been reading were just as much influenced by fashion as she was, and that she need not worry so much about doing the 'right' thing at the 'right' time.

Being confident and calm is more important than the exact time or method you choose to do things. In the long run it doesn't really matter whether your daughter is dry at night a few months earlier or later, although at the time the problem can be overwhelming. (See Chapters 11 and 12.)

If you are feeling overwhelmed by something like weaning or potty training, try and discuss this with some sympathetic parents who have been through this stage. Beware of the person who thinks there is only one way to do things because *that* way worked for them. As you know, each child and family are different, and what worked for one person isn't necessarily the solution for you.

When you are going through a difficult phase you feel as though it's lasting for ever; although other parents tell you the situation is going to change you can't believe it. You know that it's very unusual for a two-year-old to be breastfeeding or for a five-year-old to be soiling, but you feel sure you are going to be the one person who doesn't find a solution to these problems. It is very hard to keep things in perspective or to feel reassured by what other people say to you. When the problem finally disappears you will probably wonder why you felt so upset at the time.

In the first two years change is so rapid that before you have established one stage you have to rush on to the next, and you may feel it is impossible to plan ahead. But try to give yourself and your child time to get used to things. If you look ahead to the next stage in good time you can start introducing a new experience or expectation without feeling pressurized, and can give yourself and your child plenty of time to get used to the change.

Second-time parents probably find this easier because they have learned by experience. For instance, they will introduce an occasional bottle feed to the breastfed baby so that she is prepared from the start to change to a bottle, and when the time arrives she is able to accept it more easily (Chapter 11).

Planned short separations are also useful from very early days. Both you and your child learn to take separations in your stride. There is a gradual transition to longer separations with familiar people, and rarely the necessity for traumatic scenes whenever you have to leave her (Chapter 7).

How do I help my child cope with distress?

As parents you want to protect your child from stress and unhappiness; nothing is more upsetting than to know she has to face a difficulty like going into hospital, and even the thought of starting at play group can make parents feel protective (see Chapter 7).

It would be a mistake to underestimate the distress that your child can experience, but even though you can't protect her from all problems there are ways in which you may be able to help her. Introducing new experiences and the idea of them slowly, explaining them in a way your child can understand, and being consistent in your approach, are some of the ways you help your child to feel she is in a secure world and knows what to expect.

Specific fears like fear of the dark, of monsters and ghosts, or of loud noises, appear at different ages as children pass through different stages of development (Chapter 8). Other specific fears, of dogs for instance, may be related to a particularly frightening experience. Some children are generally anxious because of their personality, and may develop many fears and worries, clinginess and various tension habits with any change. One four-year-old will be delighted by starting play group and another will become extremely upset and anxious (Chapter 7).

Fears, anxieties, signs of tension are a normal part of life in children as well as in adults, and by accepting them calmly you help your child to feel that however upset she is, you are not going to be pushed off balance and will always be there to be supportive.

How do I recognize whether my child is unhappy?

Children often express their feelings in ways that puzzle adults. If they are upset they may rock themselves, hug their comforters, or go and sit in a corner; they may have a temper or become whiny and demanding. Often it is difficult to know whether your child is unhappy or just 'playing up'.

Attention-seeking can be caused by unhappiness, or by lack of limits and your child knowing that if she goes on and on she will get you to do what she wants. You have to consider whether there is anything which could be causing distress, like a new baby, jealousy of a brother or sister, or tension between parents (Chapter 2). You also need to consider whether your management is as consistent as you would like it to be (Chapter 3).

Some behaviours which you think are caused by anxiety might be part of 'normal' development, like not eating much at eighteen months, clinging at one year, nightmares or occasional rocking.

Other behaviours, like whining and moaning, make you wonder whether your child is unhappy and needs more attention from you. You may try to give her more and more of your time but find that the situation does not improve. A pattern develops in which your child wants to be with you all the time and keeps asking for things, and you do not want to upset her by saying no but begin to feel resentful about her demands (Chapter 3). Where there are no limits to your attention it is likely that your child will become unhappy and insecure, and that she will feel happier and more secure if she knows you are not going to be overwhelmed by her needs.

You know you have to put a new baby's needs before your own however exhausted you are feeling, but soon you have to begin to put some limits on what you do, otherwise the child will never be able to be independent.

Wayne had been a premature baby and had a difficult first few weeks; he also had eczema and asthma. His parents had naturally been very worried about him and he had needed a great deal of extra care. His health had improved greatly by the time he was two years old, but Wayne's mother always did everything he wanted, fussed over him at mealtimes, and followed him around all day. He was whiny and bossy with her, ate poorly and generally seemed unhappy. When his mother encouraged him to do more for himself he began to play more independently. His mother tried to stop fussing him but made sure she played with him a reasonable amount during the day and they began to enjoy each other's company much more.

Your child may be able to tell you what she is upset about, although you should be wary of putting words into her mouth, but once the matter has been discussed it is best not to keep on about it as this might increase her tension.

Why is my child difficult to handle?

Children vary enormously in their style of behaviour, in how they do things. One is slow and steady, another is volatile and erratic. Some children sail through life, others respond in ways which make it harder for them to cope.

Mary was cautious, quiet, liked to take her time in new situations, was not very sociable at first with strangers. Tim had a rather intense, excited but negative response to new situations; he liked his own way and was easily upset if frustrated. Clive was generally happy and sociable; when people were upset he didn't seem to notice.

As parents you probably look for similarities between your child's personality and yourselves or other members of the family. Heredity probably does influence temperament, but the way you behave to your child and all the experiences she has also mould her personality. Most parents learn to understand their child's personality and try to adapt to her special needs, and if your child has a difficult personality you obviously have to work harder in helping her to cope with childhood. It is harder to be sure that you are handling her the right way or to know what is causing her difficulties. Children with negative moods, with intense emotional responses, who are slow to adapt to new things, and who are inflexible in their approach, like Mary or Tim, are more likely to develop behaviour difficulties or react badly to stress.[3] Some children have particular difficulty in getting on with people and they do not seem to understand how to behave with them. They may be very shy or react aggressively because they can't seem to get the hang of how to play with other children. This can be upsetting for parents, who want their child to have friends and get on with others.

Personality isn't completely fixed, and as your child grows older she will probably become more adaptable as she gradually learns how to get on with people, and learns to understand herself.

You can't change the personality of your child, but perhaps when she is difficult it helps to realize that she is not necessarily doing it on purpose. Parents often learn by experience how best to help each child, depending on their personality. If you can also accept that your child's difficult personality is not your fault, this may help you to work out ways of helping her to cope with difficulties. (Chapter 5 and 7.)

Valerie was a very excitable girl. One moment she was reacting with extreme joy because she was playing with a favourite uncle, the next minute she would be in the depths of misery because she had to stop. She found it very difficult to change from one thing to another. Her mother found that it was best not to tell Valerie about any plans, for example, going to a party, until a short time beforehand, because she became so excited about it. It was also better not to give her too many options, such as a choice of cakes or sweets or dresses, because she couldn't make up her mind and would become very worked up when faced with quite simple choices.

Throughout the book we mention times when the child with a difficult personality may need extra attention and preparation to help her through changes and challenges.

When talking about 'your child', we have given the sexes equal treatment by using 'he' and 'she' alternately.

Chapter 2
Coping with being a parent

As you know, being a parent is an exhausting and worrying business. You decide you need to be well-organized, playful, resourceful, patient, energetic, loving and so on, but most parents are often tired, irritable and impatient, and feel failures because they can't live up to their ideals. You don't have to be perfect to be a good parent, and it is unrealistic to expect yourself or your child to be angelic all the time, or to compare yourself with other families and think they never have any problems.

There are many reasons why parents become exhausted and depressed. One important factor is not getting enough sleep. This is particularly tiring in the first few weeks of a baby's life, but can affect you however old your child. (See our companion book, *My Child Won't Sleep*.) A good night's sleep can transform your state of mind and your ability to deal with daytime problems.

Many parents lack confidence because they don't have much experience with children, but even experience isn't always a help where your own child is involved. You might expect nurses, teachers, psychologists or doctors to sail through parenthood, but they have their difficulties like other parents, and are just as reluctant to admit them because they feel they ought to manage better. It is much harder to be objective when you are dealing with your own child; your feelings are so involved, you have so much invested in being a good parent, and you feel very sensitive about any criticism or advice.

Making sure you have support from others is extremely important, and both parents have a crucial part to play in childcare and in supporting each other. If all the worry and responsibility is left to one parent this is bound to make the job of parenting more difficult. A single parent is even more in need of support from others.

Other parents can be very supportive. They are going through the same experiences as you are or they have done so in the past. They know the difficulties you are facing and they will have helpful ideas.

If you are not already a member of a parents' group, do you think it is possible to join one or start one yourself? Your health visitor or general practitioner can be helpful, and could give you the names of local parents who might be interested. As well as giving moral support, a parents' group can provide practical help like a baby-sitting rota, shopping, and even starting a toddlers' group.

In some areas there are mother and toddler groups organized by health clinics; churches also often provide these. The National Childbirth Trust is a national organization concerned with post-natal support. They often organize groups of mothers where you can meet socially with your babies, and also have special evening meetings on topics concerned with being a parent and with child-care. They will give you advice on breastfeeding and are keen to help you continue this even though you may face some difficulties. Initially you may feel very embarrassed joining a strange group of women where you don't know anyone, but the leader of the group should make you feel welcome and introduce you to other mothers with babies the same age. As soon as you start talking about your baby you will find that other mothers readily listen and say that they have had similar experiences. Swapping stories is a good way of gaining information and confidence that you are not alone. You may have heard that if you have a baby it is easy to make friends, and this is very true, as you suddenly have a very important common interest with other parents which is often the starting point of friendship.

Becoming a parent

Although you have nine months to get used to the idea of being a parent, being alone with your baby for the first time always seems to be a shock, especially if it is your first child. During pregnancy parents begin to think about a third person entering the family, but before this actually happens it is hard to imagine what it will be like.

Many couples say that having a baby will not affect their lives and that they will try to carry on as before. When they actually try to do this they face a lot of problems, and it takes time to adjust to the reality of another human being in the family who demands a lot of time and attention. It is easy to think that babies sleep most of the time, and that when they are awake they feed. But in reality the sleeps are not that long, and you find preparing feeds, changing clothes and nappies, doing the washing, cuddling and playing with your baby takes up the whole day and most of the night. You suddenly wonder where your time has gone. You have no free time left to yourself; where you had expected to lie back and have a good read or relax when your baby is asleep, you find that you are squeezing in all those jobs that have to be done before he wakes again. No wonder you feel exhausted.

There is the additional stress of actually being physically exhausted after pregnancy and birth. You may have expected to be straight back to normal but find that your stamina has diminished considerably. If the labour was long or difficult your body has suffered a major trauma and needs time to recover. If you are breastfeeding there is an additional drain on your energy supply. Many mothers feel that they don't completely return to normal until they have weaned their children, when their energy level increases again.

There are always mothers around who seem to be able to manage their child, cook good meals, have their house tidy and clean and still have time to do their make-up and manage social events. You don't have to be like that. There is probably an aspect of their lives that you don't know about, and you are reacting to the image that they are putting on for the world. They may be able to do it occasionally but then collapse for the next month.

Some mothers suffer post-natal depression, and this can be very demoralizing to them and their husbands. They had looked forward to the arrival of the baby only to feel swamped and inadequate. If you do feel very depressed then tell your doctor. It is a common problem and is nothing to feel ashamed or frightened about.

Pregnancy affects couples in different ways. They may become closer together or feel less comfortable with each other during the pregnancy. One partner may lose sexual interest in the other and this may persist after the birth. Sleepless nights and the stress of coping with a baby produce frayed nerves, and a previously good relationship may deteriorate. If a couple are not getting on their tension and unhappiness are likely to influence their behaviour to their children, who may eventually develop behaviour difficulties.[1] As time goes on parents may blame the child for these problems, or try to get the love and affection from their child which they are not getting from their partner.

One parent may get so involved with the children that they forget that they should also be working at their marriage and making sure that it is satisfactory (Chapter 7).

One advantage that a single parent has over a couple is that when there are two parents it is very easy for a child to play one off against the other. You can't help feeling pleased if you are the one your child seems to prefer, or the one who can cope best when he is difficult. Once you start competing for your child's attention or affection you will start to make him feel insecure, and you will no longer be able to guide him; he will begin to control you rather than the other way round.

Coping with stress

Stress can also affect the relationship between parents. If you are worried because of poor housing, financial problems, or difficulties at work, it is harder to be supportive to each other. Young children inevitably demand a great deal from you, and any additional stress can be very demoralizing.

The rates of depression among women with children are high. About 30 per cent of them have feelings of depression and anxiety at any one time. Having more than one child or having other worries like ill health or unemployment in the family increases the likelihood of getting depressed.[2] Not surprisingly, poor housing conditions and flat-living, especially living in high-rise buildings, are particularly stressful to mothers of toddlers.[3]

Mrs Singer was at the end of her tether living on the seventh floor of a tower block with two very active boys. They both slept very poorly and she felt exhausted and depressed. She was rehoused in a house with a garden and the situation improved almost at once. The boys slept better and could play out more, and she felt rested and happy for the first time in years.

Some parents, mothers especially, feel that they have to be able to cope with everything and should look after everyone else's needs before considering their own. This may give you a satisfying sense of doing your duty, but if you extend yourself too much you may become completely drained and find you can't even cope with everyday things any more.

It seems a good idea for both parents to make room in their lives for an activity just for themselves. This may be going out together once a week, or going to an evening class or out with a friend while the other parent babysits.

Mrs Thomas was a single parent and was quite depressed. She found it very hard to get out on her own, but she arranged with another mother that they would each babysit for a half day a week so that they could take it in turns to have time off. Mrs Thomas began to take swimming lessons and felt much happier and fitter and able to enjoy her daughter more.

Once you get depressed it becomes difficult to get out of bed in the morning, to organize your day or to initiate anything new. A timetable of daily and weekly activities may help you to get going and make sure you put aside definite times for yourself so that you can relax and feel refreshed. This sounds easier than it is, and you have to be very strict with yourself to make it work.

If you are depressed it is obviously harder to be patient with your child, respond to his needs and to provide occupation and stimulation throughout the day. His behaviour may well become more demanding and difficult, and this will add to your feelings of not managing well.

Many parents experience violent feelings of anger and rage against their toddlers when they are difficult. If you are depressed and irritable and your child is naughty the situation can feel explosive. Most women and men manage to control their violent feelings, but it is naturally disturbing to feel so out of control. If these feelings arise it may be better to try and get help than to struggle on alone. Other parents are having the same experiences and you may be able to help each other through a support or discussion group. Try to arrange an emergency safeguard for yourself so that if you feel desperate you can rush round to or phone a friend who will come to take over for a short while until you calm down. If you can admit these feelings to yourself you will immediately lessen your feelings of tension and anxiety.

If the situation seems to be deteriorating, a local under-five advisory centre, your child health clinic or a child guidance clinic may help you to break through the escalating cycle of your depression and your child's difficult behaviour. If he is not already attending one, a toddler group, play group, church group or kindergarten may be helpful. This can provide a wider social experience for your child and give you a break; and you can enjoy each other more after a brief separation. Your library, social service department, health visitor or local bookshop may have information about parent and preschool groups in your area.

Working mothers

If you worked before having your baby then you may have the choice of returning to work during the baby's first year. Some mothers do not want to work at all, are very happy to stay at home and feel fulfilled and content with their role. Other mothers may have to give up work because they do not want to work full-time and miss their baby's development but are unable to find part-time employment. When this happens it is

easy for resentment and dissatisfaction to set in, as a previously active and competent woman who was stimulated by her
job finds herself ground down by her lack of status and independence. She suddenly finds that she has no money of her
own and that her level of intellectual stimulation has fallen to
thinking about the best nappy cleanser or treatment for nappy
rash. The problem is the mismatch between her personal
expectations before the birth and the change in her existence
afterwards.

Guilt can confuse the issue, as you may feel that you should
be happy to stay at home and that your job as a mother is
vitally important, but underneath you feel bored and under-
stimulated. If you decide against working then it is very
important to find an outside interest or activity that gives you
the stimulation you need and prevents you from feeling that
your identity has been completely submerged.

Going out to work is one way in which some women renew
their energies and interest in life. They find that if they
have activities outside the home they enjoy their children
more, and are less likely to be depressed. There is no evidence that children of working mothers suffer – if they
have adequate substitute care – and there is some evidence
that they may even benefit and be more independent and
sociable.

Women with young children have to consider a number of
issues before they decide about going back to work. How
much help can they expect from their partner? If they are going
to end up doing most of the housework and child-care, as well
as outside work, this can be extremely exhausting. Some
women need the money and may have little choice about
returning to work, or about the sort of arrangements they can
make for child-care. In spite of these difficulties it seems that
going out to work on the whole is beneficial to women,
reduces the likelihood of depression and increases their satisfaction with their lives.[4,5,6]

Fathers

Fathers are becoming more involved with child-care and housework, although the major responsibility is still taken by women in most cases. It is unusual for a mother and father to share the work and responsibility equally, and more uncommon still for a man to do these jobs mainly on his own. When men do involve themselves it is clear that they have the same potential as women to be capable parents. They tend to interact differently with their children and have more rough-and-tumble play, but their care is perfectly adequate and they show the same range of parenting abilities as women[7,8].

Legislation in some countries, for example Sweden, is changing so that fathers can have more opportunities to be with their children. In some places paternity leave is now available, or parents are given a certain amount of parental time off work which they can share between them to use how they wish.[9]

Whatever your ideas about sharing roles within the family, it is certainly useful for two people rather than one to share the responsibilities, worries and decisions about child-rearing equally. You can be much more flexible if both parents can cope with the children, and are less likely to be thrown off balance if one parent becomes ill or has to go away. Your child is less likely to become over-dependent on one parent and can benefit from a close relationship with two different people.

Chapter 3
My child is whining and demanding

Children who continually whine and demand to have their parents' attention or to get their own way can be a great irritation. You suddenly find yourself shouting at them to keep quiet and leave you alone. You then feel sorry and upset at the outburst, but find that it is the only way to stop the continual requests and interruptions. Some mothers say that they feel as if they shout at their children all day long. Sometimes it is to get them to obey and at others it is to have some peace.

If you feel anxious, depressed or under tension of any sort then a demanding child can tip the balance of your self-control. You end up by screaming or giving in for a quiet life, and in that process create a more severe problem in the long run. Once your child realizes that by continually pressing her demands she can make you give way, she will continue to do this.

Part of your job is to help your child develop some elements of self-control as she grows up so that she can become aware of other people's feelings as well as her own. You can do this by teaching her to wait as well as to do what you say.

Learning to wait

One of the first steps on this long ladder is to begin to help your child learn to wait for a short while before you do what she requests. This time delay is important in regulating your child's pressing demands for immediate attention. The young child is very self-absorbed and thinks that the world and you revolve around her. Of course you can never be available all of the time, and it would be inappropriate for you always to be at your child's beck and call once she is into her second year of life. You are a person in your own right and your child gradually learns that she is a separate individual from you.

This can be a problematic stage for some parents, as they feel unable to regulate the demands of their children. They feel continually pressurized, and attempts at introducing a time delay in doing what the child requests just results in a rising crescendo of demands until the parent capitulates. The two-year-old is well on the way to understanding your separate identity, but can still be very demanding of your time and attention. You do need to be tuned into her activities so that you choose the best moments in which to encourage some self-control and patience. It is pointless to say 'Just wait a few minutes' if your child has her doll trapped in the train and can't release it on her own. Her frustration at her own lack of ability will override any attempts on your part to help her wait.

Several points need to be kept in mind:

1. Choose a suitable occasion for helping your child learn to wait. Requests for biscuits and drinks, attention and play do not always have to be met immediately.

2. Try not to use 'Wait a minute' as an expression, as your child will have no idea how long that means. Indicate the end of your present occupation, i.e. 'Wait until I've buttered the toast/finished hanging up the washing/peeling the potatoes.'

3. Always follow through what you have said. If you say 'Wait until I've wiped the table' then you must do what you promised to do. Your child may no longer be interested in her request, but you will have shown her that you fulfil your promises and given her the offer of your time or a drink. If you give in to her insistent demands then you will be teaching your child to persevere in her whining.

4. If you really mean 'no' then say 'no', rather than 'wait' hoping she will forget.

An important aspect of learning is to be aware of other people's reactions and feelings. The child who whines and cries if her parent doesn't comply immediately is not being helped to adapt to the wider world and contact with other children and adults. She can be a stressful child to have around, who can rouse her parents to irritation and anger at her behaviour, when in fact she has not been helped to learn some self-control and patience. An emotionally fraught relationship between parent and child can develop, with many instances of bad temper and clashes of temperament on both sides.

Learning to obey

Another step on the ladder of learning self-control is for children to do what their parents ask. The totally obedient and compliant child is not what most of us would like to see, but there is a fine line between encouraging your child to assert herself and yet not be disobedient. As we mentioned in the last section, she has to learn that you are an individual, and similarly you must learn that she is an individual. Mutual respect is vital to allow each of you to express yourselves as separate identities. You can't expect her to do everything you ask. You both need to develop an awareness of each other's feelings and become sensitive to the right time for making demands.

You are probably already aware of your child's different moods. Some days she will be more fragile than others. If you recognize, in the morning, that she is more clingy than normal or asking for more cuddles, then that is not the day to have a lot of confrontations. The rules that apply to you also apply to your child. If you are tense or worried about something then you are likely to lose your temper more easily or burst into floods of tears over an incident that you could have sailed through on another day.

General ideas to keep in mind when teaching your child to obey include:

1. Carry out what you say. If you make a threat then you must be prepared to carry it out. If you ask your child to stop doing something then you must make her stop. This teaches her that you mean what you say. Some children grow up learning that 'no' means 'OK, carry on'!

2. Reduce your number of commands. Many parents find

that their day consists of saying 'Leave it alone, stop doing that, keep quiet, no.' These statements are frequent and often related to trivial incidents. If you really carry through what you say, then your number of demands will decrease and there will be more cooperation from your child when you do tell her to stop.

3. Try to be consistent. Your child is likely to feel confused and possibly ignore your demands if you are not. If one day she is allowed to stand on the table, but the next she isn't, this does not teach her the reasoning behind your requests. When parents do not agree and differ in what they do and do not allow, the child can start to play one off against the other. It is important for parents to provide a generally consistent front to their child so that she learns what is expected.

4. Clearly indicate your pleasure when your child does what you ask. Your praise and acknowledgement is extremely important to her. If you comment that she is a good girl when she stops touching something when you ask her, or tidies up her toys when you say it is time to put them away, then you are helping her learn sociable behaviour. It is easy to notice the times your child disobeys you, but not so easy to notice the times she obeys.

These four basic principles are the core of all child management. We can never carry them out all the time – we are human! But it is important to be conscious of them and try to apply them in a manner which helps your child predict your reactions as much as possible. A totally unpredictable parent is the most disconcerting and disturbing element in a child's life, and can lead to quite marked and severe emotional and behavioural problems.[1,2]

Methods of handling

1. Smacking

If things have got bad enough for you to feel that hitting is the only method you have left to get your child to do what you say, then it is time to take stock of what is happening and try to change your methods. Smacking is often the result of an emotional outburst on your part, and although it may make you feel better at the time it will only result in a sobbing and resentful child who has learned to hit under stress. Children learn very little that is constructive from being hit, and if you succeed in stopping them doing certain activities in front of you they are likely to do them when you are not there. It can also make your child feel very anxious and fearful without really knowing why. She may not be sure why you are so cross.

Alternative methods of control are possible; these can be very effective, and also teach your child some self-control without her getting upset.

2. Humour

Children love games and playing, but it is difficult to be playful when you are at the end of your tether. If you can make a game out of a difficult situation then your child's teasing and boredom will disappear and you will feel more in control and relaxed. Telling your child calmly to carry on with her difficult behaviour is one way to make her see the funny side of it and decide to stop!

> Terry, aged four and a half, always complained whenever he was taken out in the car. One tactic that his parents tried was to tell him to have a good moan every half an hour for three minutes, but that moaning in between was not allowed. This method of going along with him but setting limits enabled him to be much calmer and play by himself in the intervals. When it came to his 'moaning time' he sometimes had to be reminded. At other times both he and his brother would have fun moaning as loudly as they could and end up dissolving into giggles.

Parents have to be very versatile and keep changing tactics over managing problems like this. Sometimes it helps to sing songs or promise a story after a gap without moaning, at others a sweet can be offered every half an hour on car journeys. It is important not to give in to the moaning or it will just encourage the child to do it even more.

3. Rewards

When you feel generally confident about your management approach, it is often useful to be able to rely on a fast method of encouraging your child to obey you. Giving rewards can be used for this to increase the incentive for doing what you ask. The child who messes about instead of getting dressed in the morning, the child who dawdles over breakfast, the child who won't tidy up her toys are experiences that nearly all parents have.

Sometimes you can see a pattern developing, your child starting to behave in a particularly awkward way over certain matters, at other times you just happen to be under pressure and in a rush and you want an immediate reaction rather than using your more normal patient approach. Giving small special rewards for doing what you ask can certainly speed up matters. You may well have agreed to give a biscuit when your child has eaten up her lunch, and this is part of that process. A sweet, a small cheap surprise, a sticker or a star can all be given to emphasize your pleasure in your child's behaviour. It can avoid a cycle of nagging that gradually leads to more upset as your child fails to respond to your requests.

One important consideration is to avoid getting into negotiation over rewards. If the child starts to demand more for doing what you request then you should stop the agreement immediately. Usually children start to forget or lose interest in the additional rewards after a couple of weeks and you can just gradually stop them that way. If you find that the child is very dependent on them, then start to increase the number of times she has to do what you ask before she earns her reward. This then gradually reduces her association with it.

4. Time for your toddler

These ideas must be seen in the context of a normally supportive and happy home atmosphere. They are general guidelines to the parent who is having the occasional difficulty rather than to the parent of a more severely disturbed child. Life for the preschool child tends to be tailored around the child's interests and needs, so that she has adequate contact with other children, has opportunities to play with her parents and has comforts and cuddles when she is unhappy or hurt. Some children who do not receive sufficient attention from their parents can learn to get this by being naughty. This seems to be an odd way round to do things, but parents' attention is a crucial part of a young child's life, whether it be pleasant or unpleasant contact. In these instances setting aside regular times during the day to talk to or play with your child can be a vital step in redressing the balance. It helps the child by reducing her need for attention at other times, which she usually obtains by disobedience or naughtiness.

The parents of two-year-old Neil were very keen that he should be a good boy. They criticized him all the time for minor things like kicking his feet, not sitting still, knocking some bricks over, not saying thank you. He was disobedient, although never really naughty, and it was hard for them to find anything good to say about him. It was pointed out to them that Neil had no incentive to be good, because he didn't get praise or any other attention when he was good; in fact, he got most attention for his irritating habits. His parents decided that they would try to say 'no' only about important things, and ignore trivial irritations and naughtiness. They kept a list of all the good things that Neil did and were pleased to find that there were more than they had expected. They began to pay him attention when he was not being irritating, and the whole family began to enjoy each other's company more.

Some mothers have difficulty in finding time to play with their toddler, with the pressure of housework, washing and cooking, even though they want to. A feeling of guilt and anxiety starts to build up which is communicated to the child, who proceeds to make even more demands. If you feel like this it may be important to sit down and write out a list of jobs that have to be completed and their priorities. You may have to consider not cleaning the house every day but once or twice a week, and you can occasionally have a fast pre-packed meal to give you time to take your toddler to the park or round to a friend's house to play. Your child should have playtimes with you during your day when you give her your undivided attention. If you don't do this then all of your jobs will take five times as long, as you are trying to occupy your child at the same time. You become fractious and impatient and your child becomes more clinging and whining.

Another way round the time-sharing difficulty is to plan to get your toddler involved in some of your jobs that day, whether it be washing up, making a cake or pastry, peeling the potatoes or dusting. But if you do this then you must be prepared to go at your child's speed rather than expect her to keep up with you.

5. Diaries and records of behaviour

Diaries and records can be used in two main ways:

(i) To record instances of difficult behaviour – from this information it may be possible to identify what is the matter. These records can be of parents' as well as child's behaviour. Counting the number of restrictive statements that you make during the day and comparing them to the number of times you say something pleasant to your child can be an eye opener! This can be a more rapid way of changing your reactions to your child than counting up the number of times she has been naughty or disobedient.

Another form of record is to write down examples of your child's difficult behaviour but also record the circumstances under which it occurred and your response to it. It can help you identify more clearly the behaviour that is so difficult for you to manage. It also links it to events that happen to the child. Some children only start to play up when an elder brother or sister comes home from school, or when Daddy comes in from work. Rivalry for mother's attention is a prime factor in setting off demanding or disobedient behaviour.

Setting events	Behaviour	Results
Family at breakfast table.	John ran around, refused to sit down and eat his breakfast.	Dad shouted at him and he cried but he didn't sit down or eat his breakfast.
John and Mum getting ready to go shopping.	John refused to put on his coat and ran around.	Mum lost her temper and dragged John out without his coat.

Figure 1. An example of a behaviour record.

Once you realize this is happening you can plan how to manage it more effectively.

Your reaction to the problem is vital and you may find that when you start recording your reaction it makes you aware of the number of times you do not carry through what you say. There may be a big row and upset but still there is no effect. Once the limits are set more calmly and firmly you will find that the difficult behaviour diminishes. You are still always going to be challenged as your child tests out her independence and autonomy. Sometimes it is appropriate to agree and give in, but if the bargaining and arguing start to increase then you need to set the limits more clearly again.

Tom, a three-year-old, went through a phase of refusing to put on his coat to go out in the winter. His mother had several battles with him when she had to catch him and force him to put on his coat. After a few days of this Tom realized that his mother could not be beaten and began to accept it. Although now he will put on his coat when asked, he sometimes says 'I don't need it on, it's sunny' to test whether the rule still applies.

Other parents can use a different method to ensure that the child does what they say. They may describe all the nice things they are going to do, promise a quick look in the toy shop, or buy a surprise in an effort to get their child motivated to go out. But she also has to put her coat on before she goes out. Some will just wait and not try to catch the child, who thinks that it is all a great game. Eventually the child comes back and agrees to put on her coat when she realizes no one is going to pursue her.

(ii) To record instances of good behaviour and focus on the times your child has done what you asked, or been happy and contented. This is for her as well as for you. A chart that shows her, with stars, stickers or transfers, how good she has been is a great boost. It is a visual representation of her behaviour and can be greatly valued if she has previously been told off a lot or shouted at. The process of identifying her good behaviour is important for you and gives you the opportunity to show how pleased you are with her. You can give a star for an action, for part of a day or a whole day. It is a reward as well as a record, and once she has earned it it can never be taken away from her.

One little four-year-old at a day nursery was aware of his bad temper and of the many times he was naughty and disobedient. He decided to colour in his chart with a light shade of pink when he had a good day and a dark red when he knew things had not gone well. Talking about his behaviour at the end of the day so that he could choose how to colour his chart also gave him the opportunity to hear from his teacher how good he had been. Gradually he was able to achieve a completely pink chart with his teacher's help.

	Mon.	Tues.	Wed.	Thurs.	Fri.	Sat.	Sun.
Morning	*			**	*	**	**
Afternoon		**			*	*	**
Evening				*	*	*	**
Night	**	**	**		*	**	**

Figure 2. An example of a weekly chart.

Other charts do not separate the days but may include just sticking pictures of animals or toys on to a piece of paper, or putting transfers on a spaceship scene. As long as your child is interested in it and gains pleasure from it, the style and layout don't really matter.

Chapter 4
How do I manage tempers and tantrums?

Tempers

We know as adults that some of us have a longer fuse than others, that some have bad tempers and react quickly while others seem to have endless patience. This will be the result of our general temperamental state, but also the result of how those outbursts have been coped with by others in the past.

Your child may be an irritable, rather difficult child who easily works himself up into a temper, or you may have a generally easy-to-manage child who suddenly every now and again has an incredible outburst of temper that surprises you. Most children will have shown their temper at some point by eighteen months to two years. The old wives' tale of the 'terrible twos' can be remarkably accurate for some children, who seem to become difficult and irritable at the age of about two until they begin to settle down again at three to three and a half. As always, there is an element of truth in this based on the child's developmental stage. By the age of two your child will be understanding quite a lot of what you say and will be putting words together himself. His vocabulary will have increased during the previous year and his ability to communicate his needs will be easier, using speech rather than crying and gestures. Your child will also be a very competent walker, able to be independent and experimenting quite a lot with his physical skills, climbing, riding bikes and jumping. This combination produces a child who is beginning his first real attempts at independence, and his frustration is likely to be at his own inadequacies. He will also be starting to state his will more frequently, and this inevitably leads to some clashes between you and him.

Your love and understanding is the basis of his ability to cope with the wider world. Retreat to mum or dad can be his safeguard. Your reassurance, sympathy and care will enable him to try again and to learn from mistakes or accidents. But you cannot always be the mediator between your child and his experiences; it is not appropriate that this should be so. He has much to learn through his own experiences which can be very frustrating and confusing. Inevitably, his anger will sometimes be expressed through temper as he throws the toy across the room because he cannot fit the driver into the cabin. You can help him at this stage by letting him calm down and then enabling him to try again, with your guidance and reassurance, to succeed at the task he was attempting. You may have to leave it till the next day if he finds it very difficult to cope with frustration.

Sometimes anger is expressed too readily in a manner that becomes an entrenched pattern rather than just a spontaneous reaction. Continual reaction to frustration by temper outbursts may indicate that you are trying to make life too easy for him, and he is starting to rely on you to deal with every frustration. His temper outburst results in you running to his aid, gently calming him down and then playing with him for a quarter of an hour. He begins to need you to mediate for him and help him through any slight difficulty that faces him.

In both of your interests, it is important to recognize this. The anger may be more of an act than a real temper outburst, although of course your child will not know this. His feelings are still aroused but he is in fact more in control than he and you realize. Instead of rushing in to cuddle and soothe it is sometimes wise to encourage your child to calm down by being firm and asking him to tell you what is the matter rather than yelling and crying. You go as quickly as you can to your child, but gently say 'Now tell me what is the matter and I will help, you don't need to cry to get me to come.' This said firmly and repeatedly will allow your child time to calm down but also re-learn a manner in which to cope. Your encouragement of his language and asking for your aid is one of the elementary steps in self-control that your child will learn.

Try to find the balance between helping too much or not at

all. Some children react with temper because they have not been able to learn that someone will help them.

Tantrums

Tantrums are only a more stylized form of temper outburst, when a child loses his temper for a reason and then proceeds to wild and uncontrollable behaviour. This can involve lying on the floor, kicking violently with his feet and screaming uncontrollably. Sometimes children can be in danger of hurting themselves or someone else. They may bang their hands, or throw things round the room. In the latter case some firm and gentle restraint can be necessary, where you hold your child until he is out of danger and starting to come out of the tantrum. If violence is not likely then just let your child work through the outburst in your presence without becoming involved. Losing your temper in response will have no useful effect at all and may just make matters generally worse. The important part of your involvement is to make sure that the tantrum does not have a consequence. In other words, tantrums are usually related to a child not being able to do or have what he wants. This thwarting causes frustration and anger that wells up into a tantrum. If once he has had his tantrum you then allow him to do what you initially forbade, you are teaching him a clear relation between tantrums and getting what he wants. You may feel, quite rightly, that you were wrong to say 'no' in the first place, but even so you should not give way in response to a tantrum. You can change your mind at a later point that is not linked to the loss of temper.

A tantrum can be a frightening and distressing experience for both you and your child. You never imagined the depth of anger that could well up, and it is easy for you to want to make the world better and compensate for the upset. But your firmness and consistency in dealing with the outburst will be the best security and comfort that your child can experience. If he learns that his uncontrollable rages produce marked changes in your response and that you immediately capitulate to his demands, then you expose him to the insecurity of that immense power. As long as he realizes that despite this terrible rage you will still love him and still be there to comfort him, you may be firm and calm during the outburst and when it is all over you can both make friends again.

Susan Smith was two and a half and had very severe tempers which sometimes ended in breath-holding. At these times she would lie on the floor kicking and shouting, then hold her breath and go blue for a few seconds. She had epilepsy and her parents were terrified when a temper started that it would end in breath-holding and perhaps a fit.

They always gave in to Susan, and she only had to threaten a temper for them to run to her with whatever she wanted. The Smiths wanted to stop giving in to Susan but didn't know how to go about it. Tempers were mainly around mealtimes, getting the food she wanted, and demanding food and biscuits during the day.

The plan of treatment was to put only the first course of the meal on the table, and if she started screaming to pick her up and immediately take her into the hall. Here she was to be left until she stopped screaming. Her mother stayed in the kitchen but peeped out every few minutes to check that she was all right. Susan's food remained on the table for twenty minutes and if it was not eaten then it was removed without comment. Pudding was only given if the first course was eaten.

The same procedure was used if Susan started screaming for sweets or biscuits. She was immediately taken to the hall and left before her temper became really out of control. She was only allowed a biscuit after her lunch if she had not screamed all morning, and after tea if she had not screamed all afternoon.

Mr and Mrs Smith were very frightened of letting Susan scream, but by responding very quickly and moving her into the hall they avoided a build-up of temper and made it clear to Susan that she was not going to get any attention or food by screaming. This prompt response meant that screaming brought no results to Susan, and there was little chance that the temper would build up to bring on a breath-holding attack.

The public tantrum

Some parents find that tantrums tend to occur mostly in public places. A very common point is the checkout of a supermarket, where the sweets are often displayed. Mum tends to be rather distracted trying to get out all the shopping, pay for it and pack it, so it is a prime time for the child to demand some sweets. 'No' at this point can produce an immediate tantrum, so often mothers feel under emotional blackmail. It is as if your child knows the best time to ask you when you are most likely to give in for peace. Mothers often say that their children are most difficult to manage in shops and on the bus. The looks from other people and the disapproving shake of the head are enough to make any parent feel upset.

Trying to control children in public can feel like a stage-show and the trouble is that sometimes the audience joins in. That elderly lady who says 'Oh poor dear, here let me buy you a sweet' just when your three-year-old is in the middle of a rising crescendo of crying can undermine your attempts at restraint for the next few shopping outings. Your only hope is to put on blinkers and have the courage of your convictions. If you say 'no', then stick to it come hell or high water. Fend off those 'offers of help' with a firm but polite 'No, thank you', and then either haul your screaming toddler out on to the pavement to calm down, or just stand it out until peace returns. You know that if you get harassed and cross it will just make both of you even more unhappy.

None of us is perfect, and it is easy to want to vent your own anger and frustration at this point. Why should your normally lovely child suddenly become this screaming wriggling mass just when you have your hands full, the buggy has tipped up and people are waiting for you to hurry up and pay? So many times one hears a slap and 'That will give you something to cry about.'

You can never always be a paragon of patience, but if you realize that this process is starting to recur just at these identifiable points then start to take stock of what is happening. Go to the supermarket prepared for the battle with just a few items to buy, and weather the storm with a guarded firmness and calmness. Practice makes perfect, and if you can consistently do this over three or four visits your child will learn that 'no' means 'no' and that screaming and kicking will not alter the result. Don't be tempted at any point to buy sweets to calm down your child.

Some parents are aware of this problem and may well have tried to do something about it. After having been in the habit of giving in to the temper or tantrum they begin to try and stop. They don't expect the increase in demands or anger in their child, who is just trying harder to get them to do what they normally do. Then they end up by giving in again. Unfortunately, this has the effect of teaching the child to have more severe or longer-lasting outbursts of temper or tantrum to get what they want. Instead of having an outburst that lasts ten minutes, they can have one that lasts thirty minutes. Further attempts at not giving in are then even harder and less likely to be successful.

If you do want to stop giving in to this type of behaviour, then plan when you are going to do it and be prepared to stick to it and not give in at all. If you want to give sweets then try to provide them unrelated to behaviour, so that your child does not come to expect them at certain points. It is reasonable to give sweets or crisps occasionally for good behaviour. Some parents find that giving their child a small sweet once outside the supermarket when there have been no demands and no trantrums can be a pleasant and surprising reward for the child. But don't get hooked into a pattern, otherwise your problem will have just moved out on to the pavement instead.

All parents face these difficulties to differing degrees at some points during their child's growing up. Some manage them effectively and a problem doesn't develop, while others begin to dread the outbursts and use an avoidance system, 'paying off' their child with sweets or crisps before the temper can start. This latter approach builds up the problem rather than dissipates it. Short-term gains are seen to be more important than long-term gains. If your child starts to have that level of power over you then unhappiness and insecurity can creep in. Children become unsure of how far they can go and the limits keep on being stretched in an uncertain manner. You start to feel undermined and uncertain and this affects your general relationship. You are his parent and you need to set the limits. He can then trust you and rely on you, as you have his best interests at heart.[1,2]

Breath-holding

This behaviour occurs in relation to tempers and tantrums but is another form of expression of anger. It involves a child inhaling on a breath and holding it until he turns blue and passes out. It is a very dramatic event that is distressing to parents. Your major reassurance is that your child can never damage himself through suffocation by this technique. Nature makes sure that when our brains are short of oxygen we faint. This immediately relaxes all the muscles so that breathing commences immediately before any damage can occur.

It does seem to be a very extreme form of behaviour for a child to use, but in fact, it is relatively common. Again, the important feature is for your child not to force you to change your reactions or decisions. The episode of breath-holding should not enable your child to do or have something that you would normally not allow. If the breath-holding was in relation to a frustrating event then it can be helpful to guide your child through the problem again, showing him how to cope and giving alternative methods he could use for requesting help. 'Let's try again' under sympathetic guidance can be the best opportunity for your child to learn how to control his outburst of anger and therefore learn to be more constructive.[3]

Biting

You may have had high ideals as parents about teaching your child to cooperate and share, and you get suddenly thrown by your child deliberately biting you one day, or, even worse, you hear from a friend that your child bit hers while over to play during the morning. You may feel overwhelmed with worry about how to stop this before it gets worse or out of hand. Biting often becomes a topic of conversation for parents of two- to three-year-olds, and you may worry that other parents will not invite your child to play if he has a reputation for biting. Clearly, the converse is important in that you may be unsure how to cope with someone else's child who is biting yours.

In reality, biting is no different from hitting, spitting and swearing. It is an action that is aggressive and produces a marked reaction in the recipient! A yell or scream plus commotion is quite a reaction and may be rather interesting to the child. The process of managing these events is intricately linked to your general approach to management. We often hear of parents biting their children back to indicate how painful it is. It should be your opportunity to help your child learn some sympathy and empathy for other people's feelings. Indicating in a calm manner that you feel unhappy and hurt by the bite is much more helpful than getting cross and excited about it. Your child needs to learn that other people have feelings and that they can be hurt. The manner in which you help your child when he is hurt will reflect on how he will approach you. Kissing the bad place better is something that you can both do to each other, and a cuddle to make the other person feel happy is also important. A two-year-old has a surprising amount of awareness of other people's emotions and is capable of very sympathetic and caring behaviour. Saying 'sorry' and 'I didn't mean to hurt you' is also part of social learning at this age. If you say sorry to your child then he can learn to say sorry to you.

Many toddlers will have some trial bites in experimentation. A clear message from you is important at this stage, as it will link into your reactions at a later age. A firm 'no' with a reason – 'it hurts' – and then removal of your child to a slight distance from you is likely to be sufficient.

Joan, aged two, started biting her older brother and the other children in her play group. She was not very good at sharing her toys and got very annoyed if other children interfered with her. Sometimes she bit children without any provocation at all.

Her mother had treated the biting very seriously. She had bitten Joan back and smacked her but this had not helped. It was agreed that Joan often became frustrated because her brother tended to boss her, and her mother decided to make sure they played separately at times to prevent this. If Joan bit someone she was immediately removed to a place on her own, but she was not smacked or shouted at. She was just told calmly that biting was naughty. She was allowed back with the other children when she seemed quiet.

At the play group she was encouraged to play with another girl, aged three, who did not tease her but was able to stand up for herself. The biting gradually stopped over a short period of time.

Other children initially start to bite through play.

Sarah, a two-year-old, started to bite in games. She would pretend to be a monster and go stalking her mother and then bite her on the thigh. This was initially quite funny but then the laughter produced repeat performances which ended up being painful! This was managed by firmly saying 'no' to the actual bite, with the reason, and then allowing the game to continue with pretend biting only. The parents were careful after their initial experiences not to laugh at real biting again!

Some toddlers bite when they are very excited. It is a form of expression of the excitement and can often occur when with other children. But it is important to dampen down the pitch by reacting to the bite reasonably seriously and then allowing the child to show his excitement in other ways. You can say that you know how exciting and what fun it is but that biting is not allowed.

Once children start play group then there can be an epidemic of biting. This has to be managed very carefully by the play leader, and if you are concerned then you should go and talk to her. Some children bite as a form of expression of anger and frustration, or because of deeper-seated emotional difficulties. If this seems to be the case then expert advice should be sought through your general practitioner or local child guidance clinic.

Hitting and destructive behaviour

There is a wide range of hitting that young children show, from the early shove and grab to get back a toy, to the very deliberate hits in anger and frustration of the older pre-schooler. All children will hit their parents at some point just to indicate how they feel or in experimentation. Most parents will manage this appropriately by indicating when and why to stop, and helping the child express his feelings in another way by saying 'What is the matter?'

Hitting, like biting, can easily be imitated, so if you smack your child for misdeeds you are likely to be smacked back either at the same time or at a later time in relation to another event. Children also learn hitting from each other, and you may find your three-year-old suddenly striking out in a remarkably aggressive manner, having seen this at play group. You need to be prepared for this and manage it at the time it happens so that your child clearly learns the rules of behaviour that you expect.

Hitting and destructive behaviour is normally an action that you cannot ignore. It is important to avoid children getting hurt or objects destroyed. Often a sharp 'no' and separating the children or removing the object will be sufficient, and after everyone has calmed down then is the time to discuss how the child could have managed the situation in a different manner.

If aggressive or destructive behaviour is becoming more frequent and difficult to control then it may be necessary to remove the child from the situation for a short period. This avoids the problem continuing out of your control, avoids serious hurt or damage and allows the child to calm down in safety. Removal to sit on a chair in the corner of the room or going up to a bedroom is often sufficient, and this should occur for only a few minutes. The child can then be brought back to the situation and helped to manage it in a different and more appropriate way. An aggressive reaction from you will not help, and it is vital that you stay as calm and firm as possible while managing the problem.

Aggression in other children

Many parents may face this difficulty before they face aggression from their own child. Many a mother becomes concerned when her child is hit while playing with another child. Sometimes there are social constraints on doing anything about it, as you may not like to say anything in front of the other child's mother. If this is starting to concern you then it is important to mention the problem to the child's mother and ask whether you can intervene if hitting starts. Depending on her answer you will decide whether or not you are going to maintain that particular friendship! Most parents will be very cooperative in forestalling hitting and aggressive outbursts and will be apologetic for the behaviour of their child, but you are also likely to meet the occasional parent who does not notice the problem or will not or cannot do anything about it. If this is so then you have to decide whether to intervene yourself and help your children play more cooperatively.

There is a moral dilemma posed when dealing with other aggressive children. In general we encourage our children not to hit back but to leave the child alone or ask an adult to help. But if the majority of children that your child mixes with are quite robust and easily resort to fighting, it may be important for you to help your child learn to hit back if it will avoid him being picked on and bullied. The generally accepted social rules of the group to which you belong will start to determine how you teach your child to behave.

Aggression between brothers and sisters

All brothers and sisters will fight and argue; some have physical combats while others resort to verbal methods and crying. Competition and rivalry are the obvious triggers to these outbursts, and you may feel that you are continually being called upon to be a mediator and diplomat. You will have to teach the general rule that older and bigger children do not hit smaller children, but this does not mean that the younger child can get away with provocative behaviour. You will need to decide the best method of intervention for your family. Sometimes you must leave your children alone to sort out their own battles, but at other times you need to correct an injustice. If you really don't know what happened then neither child should be allowed to do or have the prized activity or object (see Chapter 10).

Chapter 5

Is my child overactive?

As most parents discover, young children are *very* active. They seem to have an inexhaustible supply of energy – except when you want them to *walk* anywhere. They can run around from six in the morning to eight or nine at night and never seem to tire. This is quite normal; it only becomes a problem if a child lives in cramped conditions or if his energy is undirected and is not used constructively. When he does not amuse himself, cannot ever play alone, cannot concentrate on a game for more than a minute, and rushes from one thing to another without any satisfaction, then his energy and activity can develop into a real nuisance.

Martin was a tiny, impish three-year-old. He was charming but a real whirlwind, never still for more than a second. He kept touching wall plugs, turning the TV on and off, interrupting the conversation. If he wasn't watched he would take something out of the fridge, pour Vim on the bathroom floor, turn his parents' room upside down. High locks had been put on the bathroom, kitchen and bedroom doors so that he could not get into them, but he used a high stool to reach them and at times locked his mother into the kitchen.

The level of activity itself is rarely a problem. It is the aimless wandering and not being able to settle which causes problems. The commonest reason for a child being described as overactive is that he cannot direct his energy in a satisfactory way. He is continually seeking stimulation and attention from adults, and gets into mischief because he is bored.

There are wide variations from child to child in the amount of energy and activity they show, but boys are more likely to be described as restless and overactive than girls. This could in part be related to the sort of activities they prefer, like rushing around, noisy games rather than quiet ones. These differences between boys and girls might be due to the sort of games they are encouraged to play as well as to biological differences. If your child can be encouraged to like smaller constructional toys and quiet activities like books, as well as having big toys to charge around in, this will provide him with a wider range of activities, and help him develop the ability to play quietly and to concentrate. Both boys and girls need opportunities to let off steam *and* to be constructive.

Unfortunately most of us live in crowded cities, and for half the year we have cold or wet weather which makes it hard to play outside. It can be difficult to find sufficient outlets for a child's energy, and it requires careful organization every day to make sure he is kept occupied.

Overactive children often do dangerous, reckless things, like climbing on to the roof or rushing into the road. They need more supervision than average, and this adds to the difficulty of letting them out to play.

Is my child hyperactive?

Many parents think that their child is hyperactive or has 'hyperkinesis'. The term hyperactive describes a child who flits from one activity to another, acts impulsively, finds it difficult to wait or do what he is told, is fidgety and perhaps does not sleep well. *Hyper*activity has been distinguished from *over*activity. It is considered by some people to be caused by a specific disorder of attention control, that is, the child cannot attend to anything for long and this makes it hard for him to concentrate or control his impulses. Other people think that hyperactivity is just an extreme form of overactivity.[1]

Compared with the number of children who are described as overactive and restless, true hyperactivity is uncommon, at least in the UK. Many more children are described as hyperactive in the USA, and it is not clear whether this is a true difference, or just that the term is more widely applied there.

Out of every 2,000 children perhaps one will be truly hyperkinetic, whereas in a group of three-year-old children in the UK, 16 per cent of boys were described as overactive and 10 per cent of girls; 12 per cent of the boys were difficult to manage and 9 per cent of the girls.[2] Hyperkinesis is about three times as common in boys as in girls.

In practice the same methods of management are helpful for any restless, very active child.

There are several theories about the cause of overactivity and hyperactivity. One theory suggests that very mild brain damage (minimal brain dysfunction) prevents the child from concentrating and makes him impulsive and naughty. A second popular explanation is that hyperactive or restless children are allergic or sensitive to certain substances in their diet, and that this affects their behaviour.

Neither of these theories has yet been proven. Firstly, although children with definite brain damage, e.g. cerebral palsy or epilepsy, are more likely to show behaviour problems, it does not follow that all children with behaviour problems have brain damage – minimal or otherwise. Most hyperactive children show no evidence at all of brain damage. Secondly, although there is a lot of publicity about the effects of diet, the evidence so far is not convincing. Diets used for treating hyperactivity aim to eliminate all foods containing additives, artificial colourings and flavourings, in particular tartrazine and salicylates. When children are put on such a diet their behaviour often improves. But if they are then 'challenged' with various foods that are supposed to cause the difficult behaviour, they rarely then relapse to their previous behaviour. This suggests that usually it is not actually the diet which causes improvement, but the involvement of parents and children in the diet and their commitment to improvement.[3]

Studies of the effect of diet have been done mainly with children over five years of age, and we have little information about the effects in younger children.

A further influence producing overactivity could be a child's temperament; the child who has a lower attention span than average and finds it hard to concentrate will find it more difficult to conform and learn how to behave (see section on the child with a difficult temperament, p. 15).

Helping the restless, overactive child

Whatever the cause of a child's restless, overactive behaviour, the same sort of techniques might help him.

1. It is no good just telling your child to keep still all the time. If you want your very restless child to sit still, you will have to *teach* him how to do so. Start with getting him to sit for very short periods at first, even a minute if that is all he can manage, and then gradually extend the periods. Choose a quiet time and place with no distracting noises or people moving around, and try to occupy him with some interesting activity.

2. Always try to have as much of a routine as possible in the day, and set aside a certain time when your child knows you will definitely play with him. This will help to stop him demanding your attention throughout the day. You may be saying no dozens of times and then giving in, which reinforces his pattern of continual demands. You are never in a calm state when you give in like this and he never gets your full attention, and so the experience is not as pleasurable as it could be for either of you.

Peter, aged four, was very demanding and clownish. Other children did not like playing with him and he got on his sister's nerves. He never settled at anything for long, and rushed around getting into mischief all day. His parents laughed at his jokes, but these went on too long and they always ended by being irritated with him and shouting. As he was so interfering his mother never got all her jobs done and felt she never gave him her full attention. At school his concentration was poor and he found it hard to sit still. The following techniques were suggested for helping Peter:

(i) His parents would stop laughing at his jokes and clowning but would give more attention to quiet, calm behaviour.

(ii) His mother put aside fifteen minutes twice a day to

play with him, and his father thirty minutes every evening. Once Peter knew he was definitely going to have his father's attention, he learned to wait until his father had relaxed on coming home from work and stopped rushing around trying to get his attention.

(iii) The parents would not give way about things they considered important, for example, wearing a safety-belt in the car and sitting on the back seat, but if they thought a request or decision was not worth arguing about they would agree at once rather than after a scene. In this way Peter learned that no meant no, and that incessant demands or scenes would not have any effect.

Children like Peter need more order and routine in their lives than the average child. If they have to cope with indecisiveness or uncertainty they become more excited and demanding and will be harder to calm down. A regular timetable of events, perhaps put up on the wall, helps them to know the daily routine and what to expect next.

Although your child will still be more excitable than most, you may be able to help him to be calmer and more in control of himself. It may also be a help to you to know that as he grows older he is bound to calm down and improve in his concentration.

If you can avoid it, don't put your child into situations which are bound to be a strain on him or you. In situations which can't be avoided, try to prepare beforehand. If you are going on a journey, visiting friends or if friends have come to see you, try to find some special interesting activity for your child and promise a special treat if he behaves well.

John found it very difficult to be quiet and let his parents talk when they went visiting, and they decided to adopt the following routine.

They started with short visits which were gradually lengthened, and John was told he could have a special treat at the end of the visit if he had been quiet – usually a story. He had a game which he really liked which was kept specially for visits, and his father took him out for a short walk in the middle of the visit if he could not play in the garden.

The technique of providing a special treat or a star for being calm can be used for train and car journeys, shopping, or any other situation where it is hard for your child to sit still or be quiet. Gradually he will learn that he can cope with these frustrating situations and you can stop using the rewards.

Should I use a special diet?

As we have already mentioned, it is still far from certain that a special diet is helpful for overactive children, but you may feel convinced that your child is allergic or sensitive to something he eats and want to try the effects of dieting. Before committing yourself to something which is expensive and frustrating to your child, it is worthwhile trying the effects of a change in your management. Even if you are going ahead with a special diet it is still important to be as consistent and firm as you can be with your child.

If you are trying the effects of food, you will have to put your child on a very limited diet, free from all the things you suspect are the culprits. If his behaviour definitely improves on the diet this *might* be an indication that certain foods affect his behaviour. The only way you can be sure is by adding each suspected food separately to the diet. If his behaviour definitely deteriorates when 'challenged' with these certain foods, this would be strong evidence that dietary factors are important. As you can see, this is a time-consuming business, and it is often extremely difficult to know whether improved behaviour is related to diet. In our opinion the number of children likely to be helped by a diet is probably very small, but you may feel that anything is worth trying if your child is really difficult to manage.

Some children have become malnourished when taking a special diet, so if you do decide to keep your child on a diet, do make sure he is having enough to eat, with varied foods and adequate protein, fat, calories and vitamins.

Should I use drugs?

Drugs are widely used in the USA for the child who is restless, naughty and finds it hard to concentrate. In the UK their use is much more limited; there is a general attitude that it is not a good idea to give drugs to young children for long periods and that if you can help a child by altering his management and your responses to him this is much more satisfactory. It is helping him to control himself rather than using drugs to do so.

Studies have shown that the drug most widely used (methylphenidate or Ritalin) definitely helps to improve concentration even in children without any particular problems. If concentration improves, a child is less impulsive and restless, learns more easily and is generally calmer.[4]

If your child is very excitable and uncontrollable he *may* be helped by the use of a drug, but even so, consistent management remains of major importance.

Chapter 6
How do I cope with habits?

Habits are quite common in young children. Seventeen per cent of three-year-olds have three or more habits, and 14 per cent of four-year-olds. These habits mostly clear up by the time a child is at school, and they are not usually a sign of emotional disturbance. Only if your child devotes long periods of the day to masturbation, rocking or other habits, and shows several signs of disturbance, should you consider getting further advice.

We have divided habits into comfort and tension habits, although the two groups have some resemblances and are not clearly distinct. Habits of both types tend to increase at times of tension, and are likely to occur more frequently if they are paid a great deal of attention.

Children who are retarded or visually impaired tend to develop habits easily. It is more difficult for them to occupy themselves and they are often bored, so they resort to some form of comfort or tension-releasing behaviour. Response to their habits should be the same as for any child.

Comfort habits

Parents soon discover that actions such as rocking a child in their arms, patting him, or singing lullabies, are excellent ways to soothe a child to sleep (see our companion volume, *My Child Won't Sleep*). Monotonous rhythmic stimulation is very calming to children and they have an innate biological response to become drowsy when it occurs. When children get older they develop their own means of soothing themselves, and these usually involve some rhythmical movement like thumb-sucking, rocking, stroking something soft, sucking a dummy or bottle; these comfort habits are most likely to begin to appear between six and eight months of age.[1]

Habits tend to occur at certain times such as settling to sleep, at times of upset or stress and when bored. Children who have a special blanket or toy will often hold this during the day if they are upset or in a strange place. These actions or objects act as a comfort and as a substitute for the mother and father when they are not around to provide comfort.

A comfort object can remain in use for years and years, even up to the early teens, and this is usually not a sign of emotional disturbance.[2]

Other means of comfort which frequently develop are rituals. The bedtime ritual is an extension of bedtime comforting habits. It is not a problem unless it interferes with settling because it goes on for so long. Rituals are a way of bringing order into the sometimes confusing world of toddlers. They usually clear up, but if your child is developing more and more rituals this may be a sign that he is generally anxious.

Giving up the comforter

The use of a soft comforting object like a blanket or toy is highest in the second year and declines after this.[3] Children generally give up their comfort object gradually, and you may want to encourage this as it can be awkward carrying a blanket or toy around everywhere. If the comforter gets lost or left behind when you are visiting this can create chaos because without it your child cannot get to sleep.

If the object is very big, like a whole cot blanket, you could gradually make it smaller or even cut it in two so you have half in reserve when it needs washing. Some blankets just get smaller and smaller as time goes on, and they wear away until only a strip is left which eventually just disappears.

When your child starts play group it may be a good idea for him not to take his comforter with him; it is bound to get lost there. Encourage him to keep it for home use, especially at bedtime. Some parents just throw the comforter away when they think it is too smelly or too old to wash any more. If you do this you run the risk of your child being upset and unable to get to sleep, although most children seem to accept it eventually.

Thumb-sucking

Thumb-sucking starts quite early on in life, as soon as the child can get his thumb into his mouth. He is more likely to suck his thumb if he falls asleep without the breast or bottle and is put to bed awake.[4] Thumb-sucking is not a sign of inadequate opportunity to suck, it is merely one of the comforting habits most likely to develop. In one way it is a most convenient habit, because it is very easy for a child to use and avoids parents having to hunt round for a dummy or bottle all the time. On the other hand, dentists definitely disapprove of thumb-sucking because it can push the front teeth forward.[5]

Many children continue thumb-sucking until they start school or even longer. This does not matter as long as your child is happy and active most of the time. If he spends long periods in a sleepy state, doing nothing but sucking his thumb, then either he needs other activities and more stimulation, or he is miserable or tense a lot of the time and needs more comforting from you. It may help to sort out why he gets so tense and upset; if the situation can be made easier for him, the thumb-sucking may diminish.

You may feel that your child's thumb-sucking is excessive and is damaging his teeth and that you would like to stop the habit if you can. A number of different techniques have been tried out successfully.[6,7] Every time your child starts sucking his thumb you could make a game asking him to clench his fists for three minutes instead. Eventually the older child, over four, will be able to tell himself to clench his fist without you being involved at all; the younger child will need reminding by you. This technique can also be used for nail-biting.

Another method is to reward your child for not sucking his thumb. You could start by giving him a star after an hour if there has been no thumb-sucking, then gradually extend the length of time which has to be free of the habit before he can get a star.

Head-banging and rocking

Being rocked is one of the most comforting actions for a child, and even adults rock themselves when they are upset. It's not surprising that once he can rock himself a child will do this 'just for fun'. Head-banging may be added because it also is pleasurable. By the end of the first year there are very few children who do not sometimes rock or head-bang.[8,9] Rocking or head-banging only turn into problems if they become ways of getting attention or important sources of comfort, although if one of these behaviours is selected by your child as a soothing mechanism for settling to sleep it can be a nuisance and difficult to stop. (See *My Child Won't Sleep.*) In some children head-banging is a sign of tension and occurs when they are worried or upset.

> Jane, aged five, was banging her head so violently that she was at risk of hurting herself, but she only did this in the presence of her parents. She was one of four young children and the parents were finding it hard to cope with them all. Jane was the quietest one of the family, and had appeared happy to be left to her own devices. She had begun to bang her head when she had an attack of earache, and when this drew her mother's attention to her she banged even more.
>
> The parents decided to ignore her head-banging completely (although this was difficult to do) and to give her much more attention but only when she wasn't head-banging. At first the banging increased as Jane found it was ignored, but when she realized she got plenty of attention without banging, the habit gradually disappeared.

Bad tempers when frustrated may include regular head-banging. The effective response to this is the same as with tempers, that is, not to give way to them, however severe they are. Once you give way you are only encouraging your child to bang harder to get what he wants.

> Three-year-old Clive had frequent bad tempers and banged his head on the door whenever he was thwarted. His mother always gave way in the end, so the tempers were successful

and he got what he wanted. She decided to ignore the head-banging and never to give in to him when he started, which was successful. She expected that the head-banging would probably *increase* at first when he was ignored, as Clive tried harder to get his way.

Handicapped children, such as those with visual impairment or slow development, are more likely to have various habits like rocking or head-banging. It is harder for them to amuse themselves or be happily occupied, and parents have to work harder at making sure they are not bored or unhappy. Because it is harder to look after them, there is a tendency to leave them be when they *are* quiet, and it is then that they may start some comfort habit. Even though your child is handicapped, the principle of management is exactly the same as with other children. If you are prepared for this type of behaviour you may even be able to stop habits becoming entrenched by distracting your child and providing alternative satisfactions and amusements from his early months.

Masturbation

This is a behaviour that often disturbs parents a lot because it is socially embarrassing. Children inevitably explore their bodies during the stage of toddlerhood, and most of them find that the genitals are particularly pleasurable to touch or that rubbing the thighs together is pleasurable. This is a natural stage in development. It is quite normal too for boys to have erections. Although children may go through a stage of rubbing their genitals more frequently in public than you would like, generally this does not become a problem. As with any habit, there are certain situations in which masturbation may become problematic. If you begin to pay a great deal of attention to masturbation and draw your child's attention to it, he may begin to do it more frequently to gain your attention or to tease you. If the masturbation is irritating you, it is better to give him something else to do, or perhaps suggest he goes into his bedroom, than to nag about it. With the older child it may be better to explain that this activity should not be done in public.

If your child is bored or unhappy he may find that masturbation is the best comfort he has. There is no point in telling him to stop unless you are going to deal with the problem of boredom or unhappiness. Tension between parents can lead to a tense family atmosphere and the child may masturbate to soothe himself; he then finds that this brings him a lot of parental attention *and* seems to stop his parents quarrelling while they talk about him, so he continues the habit with even more persistence.

John, aged four and a half, masturbated a great deal, and when friends visited his parents were very embarrassed and angry. The parents had very different ideas on family life and on bringing up children and were getting on badly. John was often lonely and bored. His father did not play with him or give him much attention and his mother fussed over him a lot to make up for this. The parents, especially the father, decided to pay as little attention as possible to John's masturbating but to give him more attention at other times. Only when his parents were able to work out a compromise on their ideas, and his father especially was giving him more affection and less nagging, did John stop masturbating so often.

It is unlikely that a child who has plenty of love and affection is going to masturbate excessively either for comfort or to get attention.

Tension habits

Other habits appear to be more a result of tension than to have their origin in comforting behaviour. These include nail-biting, stuttering and stammering, licking the lips, picking at scabs or sore places, nose picking, tics and hair-pulling. These habits often occur when your child is concentrating on something, for example, watching TV, and is not really aware of what he is doing. You may be able to identify the cause of a tension or anxiety, and dealing with this may stop the habit. Often there is no obvious cause for the habit to start, but once it gets going it becomes entrenched and hard to stop. If your child develops one of these irritating and worrying habits, your spontaneous reaction is to tell him to stop doing it. This *may* be effective, but often the more attention that is drawn to the habit the more tense your child becomes. He may stop for a short while after you have told him off but he will then start up again. It is probably more effective to ignore these habits and try to distract him by giving him something else to do.

Stuttering and stammering

As they learn to speak, most children have difficulty in pronouncing certain words or syllables. They may stumble over some words, hesitate over others, try to speak in a rush, or become excited and not get their words out at all. Most children stammer or stutter (say the same sound or syllable over and over again) at some time. Some parents tease or criticize their children when they don't speak properly, and this may make them more self-conscious and make the stammer worse. It's better to help your child to calm down and be less excited. Tell him to pause, take a breath and speak slowly if he is getting into a tangle, but don't draw attention to his stammer.

If your child has other signs of tension and anxiety it may help to pay attention to the causes of these, such as starting nursery school or the presence of a new baby. It could be that your child is extra-sensitive and likely to feel anxious or excited without particular cause (see the section on temperament, p. 15).

Stammers occur more often in boys and seem to be related to immature development.

The chances are that your child will grow out of the stammer, but if it seems to be persisting, say for longer than nine months, it could be helpful to discuss the problem with a speech therapist, who can be contacted through your child health clinic.

Tics and other movements

As they grow, children experiment with moving their muscles, especially their mouths and tongues. They like to pull faces in front of the mirror or to tease each other and their parents with funny faces. If these grimaces or movements are given a lot of attention, your child might begin to do them more and more.

> Patricia used to turn her lower eyelids inside out. She looked quite bizarre when she did this and it used to drive her parents frantic. It was certainly hard to ignore the behaviour, which is what we advised and which was eventually a successful method of treatment.

Tics are repetitive, useless movements involving a small group of muscles. They are most common in children aged between six and seven, and rarely start before four years of age. Boys are affected more than girls, and the tics may be a sign of anxiety or tension. They seem to be involuntary, but children can often stop them for a while if told to; they often occur when a child is concentrating on something. Frequently one tic lasts a few weeks or months, then disappears only to be replaced by another. The commonest tics include blinking, sniffing and jerking the head. Eventually the majority of children grow out of their tics, but they can be irritating and worrying.

Parents are often uncertain whether they should ignore these movements and tics, or whether they should tell the child to stop, and this can be a difficult decision. Sometimes sharply telling a child to stop will inhibit the behaviour, but often increased attention seems to increase the habit. One form of treatment which seems paradoxical but does work for some older children is to tell them to 'practise' the habit or tic energetically for five minutes several times a day. This may have the result of making a child more aware of doing the habit and of inhibiting it.

Conclusion

The best way of dealing with habits is to ignore them and not get emotionally worked up about them. If your child is bored, provide him with more activities and interests. If he is miserable or tense, try to deal with the cause of this rather than just trying to remove the symptom.

If the habit has become well established, make a determined effort to ignore it and give your child a lot of attention when he is not showing the habit. You may find a star chart or animal chart helps to motivate your child to try harder, for instance not to bite his nails or pick scabs.

Chapter 7

How do we cope with being apart?

Many parents, especially mothers, are surprised how difficult it is for them to be apart from their young baby. In the first few months of life you are spending all of your time with your baby, you become very attached to each other and feel a strong sense of loss when you are apart.

Ideally, being apart will gradually develop at a pace that suits you and your baby, so that by about six months you can leave the baby in the care of your husband or relative for a few hours without upset.

Babies react preferentially to their mothers soon after birth, but some time after six months of age they begin to show more marked signs of preference for people they know well. From about nine months your baby may become more clinging and attached to you or to the other people who look after her regularly. This is a normal phase of development, although children vary in the amount of upset they show. Some never seem to go through this stage at all. Your child's personality and temperament may affect the degree to which separations affect her at this time. Her previous experience is also very important. If she has had some pleasant and successful separations in the past then she may be less dependent on one person through this phase.

The fear of being separated from you is often a very wearing experience if you can do nothing without your child in your arms or very close to you on the floor. Suddenly your personal time, even for going to the toilet, is totally invaded by a howling distressed baby.

The intensity of this anxiety about separation is quite surprising to many new parents. You have already experienced the loving and playful feelings, the anger and discomfort, but this fear and worry is new. Your methods of managing it will be important in helping your child cope with the later fears that she will experience. Irritation and anger can only make the situation worse, with your baby reduced to a screaming, distressed bundle wanting your love and comfort even more. If your baby is unable to crawl then she cannot follow you and is dependent on you taking her with you. Often the advent of crawling can revolutionize your child's ability to manage her fear and anxiety. She is able to control the world a little more, and as long as you don't flit around too fast she can manage to keep you in sight. This stage of development requires a lot of compromise on your side to achieve a reasonably calm and pleasant day. You need to tailor your activities to what your child can stand. If you have several jobs to do first, cut them in half or you will feel frustrated at not getting everything done, then try to plan several jobs in one room at a time so that you don't end up rushing up and down stairs with a clinging baby attached to you.

Avoiding too much upset is the best way of surviving this stage. As your child grows she will become more able to manage herself through her ability to walk and talk. The fear of separation may still be there, but is coped with by finding you when she needs you. The two-year-old still calls out to find out where you are when you go into the bathroom to wash, and has a tendency to follow you up and down stairs unless very preoccupied with playing. Brothers and sisters can reduce the level of dependency on you, as they provide company and interest when you are not in the room. A distracting activity or toy can occupy her for a while, although once she realizes you are not there, nothing is likely to pacify her except you.

Infants do not necessarily show most clinging to their mothers, they also become very attached to their fathers and often go through inexplicable phases regarding whom they cling to. They may cling to mum for several months and then insist that dad carries them around all evening instead. It is very important for both parents to share as much as they can so that one parent does not feel left out. Keep in mind that these phases are temporary, and that as your child gets older she will probably not be so 'temperamental'.

Separation from toddlers

Many mothers mention that their child clings and cries all morning while they are trying to do their housework and chores, but after lunch, when they are prepared to sit down and play, their toddler will sit with them for only a few minutes and then toddle off to play on her own. If you look at this from the child's point of view, her haven of security is on the move in the morning so she has been keeping in contact as much as possible. Once mum has settled down she can then feel able to do the things she wants to do as long as mum stays put. As in all aspects of coping with children, there is a balancing act between your needs and your child's needs. Sometimes the scales will swing more one way than the other, but as long as they are not permanently down on one side then you are likely to be doing a good job.

Changes in your child's surroundings can take you back a few stages in her ability to cope without your presence. A move of house, or a holiday in a strange place, can increase your child's demands to be with you continually. She feels less certain of finding you on her own, as she may not know her way around, so a tolerant response from you is important to help her feel secure. You may feel that she had started to grow out of her all-encompassing need of you, only to see it resurrect itself. A new environment is a form of stress on a child, and as you expect your child to come to you when she is upset or hurt, then she will seek you out when unsure or fearful of a situation. Encouragement to help her gradually explore with you will help, but try not to go too fast. Allow your child to become familiar with one or two rooms before introducing the whole house plan.

Elizabeth, aged fourteen months, was content to accept playing on her own downstairs for up to five minutes without her mother's presence. She had just mastered walking and was a mobile crawler. The family moved to a much larger house which required much renovation. The disturbance of the move and the level of excitement upset her to a degree. She seemed to find it strange to see her own familiar bedroom furniture and toys in a strange place, and took a long time to settle to sleep the first evening.

After the move she found it difficult to go to sleep for the first three nights, and took about two weeks to become familiar with the new house. She would not let her mother out of her sight for the first couple of days, and then would not let her go up and down stairs without her for about two weeks.

The size of the house seemed an important factor, because although she had been on holidays previously, they had been in smaller accommodation where her parents were always very close by.

To help your child cope with your absence, there are several pointers to be kept in mind:

1. Always tell your child when you are going out of her sight or presence.[1] This provides reassurance and information right from the beginning. Say briefly what you are going to do, and stay away for only a few seconds initially, building up the absence to a few minutes as your child is able to manage. By doing this you are gently teaching your child to manage without you. You are also helping her learn to anticipate your actions so that you are predictable. Your child will cling to you more if she is not certain about what you are likely to do.

2. Always indicate that you are coming back. Try to get back before she starts to cry; this will mean that she has reached the end of her ability to wait without you, and if this happens too much then the time will shorten rather than lengthen.

3. Match your expectations to your child's age. It's pointless telling your six-month-old that you are popping upstairs to fetch the dirty clothes, but it is appropriate for a one-year-old who has some understanding of language.

Leaving your child with babyminders, friends and relatives

The fear of separation that develops in the first year of life does not mean that you can never leave your child, but if you do want to encourage some independence, or if you are going back to work, then helping your child adjust to the new person is very important. Research indicates that babies do not have to be looked after only by their mothers, and as long as there is a consistency in the pattern of who looks after them then they can settle and be contented.[2] The worst problem for a young child to face is being looked after by lots of different people, with no understanding of where mummy is or when she is likely to return, so the child's whole basis for security is lost. Children who have had many different caretakers sometimes become rather withdrawn and inappropriately self-sufficient, or search continually for social contact and make indiscriminate emotional links with anyone with whom they may come into contact.

Many mothers who want to go back to their jobs will return to work when their child is about six months old. Some return much earlier, depending on their maternity rights in the organization for which they work. The issue of separation then becomes a very important one. Returning to work when she is six months old is easier for your baby to manage than if you leave it until she is in the nine- to ten-month clinging stage. This does not mean that your six-month-old won't miss you. You are still the centre of her world and her smiles and response to you will be unlike her response to anyone else, but it is possible to hand over her care to another person, whom she can get to know well. The important feature for your baby is to be able to understand events around her as far as possible, and to do this she needs to be able to learn the reactions and responses of adults around her. If there are too many adults this process of learning becomes confused, and the child feels she cannot influence or control her environment. She also cannot communicate her needs sufficiently, as the adults do not learn her signs and signals. If possible you should aim to have one other person who will look after your baby for you on a consistent and regular basis. This will help compensate for your absence, and you will feel happier knowing that your baby will get to know her minder well.

Introduce the minder slowly, so that your child gets to know her while you are there. Once the child shows some confidence in the minder's presence you can then try to leave her for short periods. You may find that the process of saying goodbye will be difficult, but that your child settles down when you have actually gone. It is as if children feel they can stop you going while you are saying goodbye, but that when you have gone there is no point in crying.

If your baby starts to show marked signs of distress, for example, becomes excessively clingy towards you, is withdrawn or listless, cries a lot when you are not there, develops sleep disturbance and goes off her food, then it is important to reconsider the minding arrangements. It may be that the minder is not providing good care and attention. With a marked change in routine your baby will show signs of disturbance, so it is important to ensure that the minder knows your routine and carries that out in much the same way to begin with. Also make sure that your baby is being played with and cuddled to the extent that you would like.

Starting play school or nursery

Some children start play school or play group for a couple of mornings a week at the age of two and a half to three. Other children have to wait until they are four or five to join the nursery of a school. Usually there is a gradual increase in the length of time and the number of days' attendance, so that the child gets used to the new surroundings and doesn't become too overtired. Mothers are usually encouraged to stay for the first couple of sessions to settle their children, and perhaps go out for up to fifteen minutes during that time to see how their child reacts to being left. You should tell your child that you are leaving and when you are going to collect her. As time is a meaningless concept at this age, saying 'I'll see you at milk-time or dinner-time' can often be helpful. The reassurance that you will be there to collect her is important, and if you can't be there then say who will meet her so that she doesn't feel confused and upset.

Sometimes the suggestion of your child painting a picture to bring home with her will tide her over the separation from home, and a happy link between home and play school is forged. It can be helpful to arrive early to collect your child after the first couple of sessions, so that she can show you what she has done during the morning if there are any difficulties. This helps the child feel that you know what she is doing. Don't describe all the exciting things that you have been doing while she has been at play school, or she will want to stay away and do them with you!

Some children take a long time to settle at play group. Their mothers may have to spend a term trying to settle them in. Others take to it like a duck to water and it comes at just the right time.

It helps if you can get used to separation earlier. (Many nursery school teachers comment that it is the mums and not the children who find the first separations difficult and tearful.) As school is compulsory at five, only at this age do some of the more reluctant mothers face being apart from their children.

Problems with separation

Most non-working mothers will expect to be able to leave their two- to three-year-olds for a period of about two hours while playing at a well-known friend's or relative's house. This is a rough guide for a child who is used to having you at home all day with her. Many mothers will spontaneously start small crèches for this age group, where the children can enjoy playing together under the supervision of one or two mums while the other two mums go shopping for a couple of hours. Certainly when you are visiting friends you expect your child to be able to play apart from you for a short period. These short separations are important for both you and your child, and if they do not seem to be spontaneously developing then it is important to think why. There are several reasons that can adversely affect the ability of your child to tolerate your absence.

1. Illness

If your child is sickening for something or is ill then she is unlikely to want to be left without you. Even the most independent children become very 'mumsy' when they are ill. Mum is usually the only person who can look after them.

2. Birth of another baby ·

Often the first child in a family is in her second year when another baby is born. This can sometimes generate jealousy and competition for mother's attention, so trying to leave your child at this point and go off with the new baby is unlikely to be greeted enthusiastically. Sometimes the father, grandparent or other relative can come into their own at this stage and make a special fuss of the older child, so that she thinks going to granny's is something very special rather than a separation from mum.

3. General immaturity

Not all children develop at the same rate. Slight development delay during the first couple of years of life is not particularly indicative of later problems, but it will influence the rate at which your child will be able to cope with normal changes. If your child is slower than average to walk and talk, then she is likely to be slower in her emotional development as well and may not be ready for the phase of separation yet.

4. Stresses in the family

Children are very responsive to any emotional problems between their parents or in either parent. Anxiety that is generated by this can influence your child's feeling of stability and consequently her ability to leave you.

5. Parental management

If your child is used to ruling the roost at home, then she is likely to try to continue this when you attempt to leave her. If you find difficulty in setting limits for her general day-time or night-time behaviour at home, you will be unable to say 'Goodbye, see you at tea-time' and expect her to accept it.

6. *Unhappy or unsuccessful previous separations*

Past events will influence how your child reacts now, and if perhaps you have been ill and suddenly unavailable to her under mysterious circumstances, or if she has had to go into hospital, she may feel very cautious about leaving you again. Certainly the handling of these events will have had an important bearing on her present reaction, as we discuss in the next section. Also, if she has been left somewhere or with someone that she has not liked, she will be more fearful.

Peter Timms was a lively three-year-old when he was with his mother but he found it very hard to separate from her even at home. Whenever visitors came or she went visiting he was particularly demanding of her attention, and hung round her rather than playing with other children. He had never been separated from his mother for more than a few minutes. She felt he was missing out on the opportunity to play with other children, and also wanted him to stay with others so that she could go for hospital appointments or shopping without him, as he became so bored and restless in these situations.

Mrs Timms began by leaving Peter for five minutes with a good friend whom Peter knew well. She told him she was going to post a letter and would return in five minutes, which she did. She then gradually lengthened her periods of absence, always explaining clearly to Peter what was going to happen and always returning when she had promised. Each time she said goodbye to Peter calmly and left promptly, so that there was no time for a scene to develop. Although he protested, he soon became used to the separations and accepted them happily.

At home Mrs Timms encouraged Peter to stay in one room for five minutes while she went into another room to do something. She set a timer for five minutes and said that when it rang Peter should come and find her. Peter enjoyed this game, and gradually the times apart lengthened without any difficulty. He began to enjoy the company of other children more, and was able to play with them while his mother talked to her friends.[3]

Going into hospital

Many children under five are likely to have a hospital admission, and a growing number of hospital toys and books is becoming available.[4] Your child needs as much preparation for this experience as you do, and although many children's hospitals try to make facilities available for you to stay with your child, it may not be possible because of lack of space, or you may feel too committed to your other children and husband to be able to stay with her.

There are several guidelines that are worth keeping in mind when preparing for the admission.[5,6]

1. Tell your child a couple of days before she is due to go in so that you both have time to talk about it. A little bit of worry beforehand can help her manage much better when it actually happens.

2. Tell her simply about the arrangements of the ward, with nurses and doctors and other children in bed. Show her pictures and play pretend hospital games with her toys to imitate it.

3. Indicate simply what is the matter with her and what is going to happen. This has to be tailored to your child's age, but information about the area of her body to be treated and whether it will hurt or be sore will be useful. Sometimes a practice on a doll or teddy can help.

This will give your child some information on how to anticipate the experience. Don't try to alarm her or frighten her by becoming too technical or detailed, but don't take her there pretending she is going to visit her great-aunt. If she shows a little concern don't be alarmed, you can't pretend that it is a totally pleasant time. She has to know what she has to face and this is much better than hiding it from her.

Things to do at the admission are:

1. Take in a favourite toy or her comforter/blanket. Also her dummy or bottle, even though you feel she should have outgrown them.

2. Tell the nurses about your special words for cuddling, saying good night, or going to the toilet. Also tell them her nickname and the foods that she likes and dislikes.

If you are unable to stay in hospital with your child then try to be predictable about your visits. Never say you are coming to see her and then fail to turn up if you can possibly avoid it.

Hospital stays can be great fun for some children. They enjoy the contact with other children and all the fuss and attention. But don't be surprised if even though she appears to have managed well, she may start to bed-wet again or show disturbed sleep when she gets home. There is sometimes a delay in the child's reaction, and even though you have fully prepared your child to the best of your ability she still seems clingy and upset afterwards. Providing reassurance and comfort through this phase of re-adjustment and memory is all you can do. Don't start feeling guilty at this stage, as it won't help either of you. All parents would prefer to avoid a hospital admission for their child if possible, and your job now is to help her gently back into her old routine. Talking about what happened to her can help her think about the events, and perhaps acting it out with her toys can help her express some of her fears and feelings in play.

Chapter 8
How do I help with fears and worries?

Fears and worries are part of growing up. There are specific fears related to different stages of development, and fears that are suddenly generated by an unpleasant experience.[1,2] Some incapacitating fears can be long-lasting.

Children's fears change as they develop. The very young baby is amused by strange faces and noises. At around six months she is well able to tell the difference between familiar faces and strangers. Beards, spectacles, deep voices, odd noises, may suddenly begin to frighten her. As she gets older she will gradually become more used to strangeness and will begin to enjoy novel things again.

As fears of sudden noises and unfamiliar objects fade, new fears can develop. Many toddlers develop fears of the dark, insects, dogs, the noise of the vacuum cleaner, thunder or water. These are extremely common in toddlers; most have one or two fears and about 10 per cent will have three or more fears.[3] Unless your child shows several other signs of anxiety, such as frequent nightmares, reluctance to let you out of her sight, many worries about trivial things, her fears should not cause you concern. Some children are temperamentally sensitive and go through periods of fears and worries in the pre-school stage. You will have to be particularly patient and gently encourage your child to be more adventurous and independent if she is like this. It is important to make sure that you are not contributing to her anxieties by showing her what a worrier you are and by parental quarrels which make her feel insecure.

It is quite usual for three- and four-year-olds to ask questions about death, illness and separation, and by answering these questions as fully as you can at a level your child can understand, you will help her to cope with these puzzling aspects of life. If you fob off your child with 'I'll tell you when you are older', she may become worried by these unknown and forbidden mysteries.

Mary, at the age of two and a half, was quite puzzled by a graveyard on visiting a church one day. She asked what the gravestones were, and when she was told that they showed where a dead person was buried in the ground, this generated a series of questions like 'Will they get up again? Can they come out?', and some intensive looking on top of a grave to see where the person was. Her mother then talked a little about death to her, using her knowledge of plants and flowers dying and explaining that they do not come back again. A couple of days later, when passing the churchyard again in the car, she gaily pointed out to her father 'Oh, that's where all the people are in the ground.'

The boundary between feelings of fear and those of excitement is very narrow. Many games played by children involve an element of surprise or fear. You know that when you play stalking monsters with your two-year-old there is a fine edge between the excited shriek as she enjoys being chased and the sudden cry of fear. 'That's enough' can mark your child's ability to stop you going too far. Be careful not to go too far in this teasing, particularly dads, who often enjoy these games. Jumping out and startling games are also part of this; your child is surprised and mildly frightened but copes with the feelings in the context of fun.

When a fear grows to the level of seriously disturbing your child's normal behaviour then it is termed a phobia; for instance, a child may be so terrified of the noise that lorries make as they go past that she may refuse to leave the house to go shopping in the buggy. Another child may be so frightened of flying insects that she refuses to go outside in the summer time. These feelings may start from an unpleasant experience that unduly frightened and upset the child. The association between the event and the feelings become interwoven, so that just a thought or talk about the feared object can create intense anxiety.

Parents' fears

Children often pick up their parents' fears. The sight of a panic-stricken mother can seriously upset a child, so that the anxiety created is rapidly linked to the large spider that is coming stalking across the carpet. There has been much speculation that the frequency of insect and snake phobias in human beings far exceeds the possible number of bad experiences with them. This leads on to the idea that we may have a special vulnerability to them, rather like the idea that baby rabbits have an inborn fear of falcon shapes hovering over their heads.

Many parents try desperately not to show that they are frightened by certain events and objects, knowing that this could alarm their children. The thought of your four-year-old tenderly carrying a matchbox in from the garden, saying 'Mummy, look, I've got a surprise for you', is enough to set any mother's hair on end, knowing that the box contains a spider or an insect. All you want to do is scream 'Get that out of here', but you try to say calmly 'Oh, lovely, dear, thank you. Perhaps I'd better let him go outside now.' If you show your fear in front of your child she is likely to think there is really something to be frightened of, and to lose her burgeoning interest in how things work and grow.

Phobias

Phobias are often linked to specific experiences. Dogs are a very common phobia: their size, the barking and jumping unexpectedly are all aspects that can terrify a young child. Some parents may foster a healthy caution of dogs, in that they stop their children indiscriminately going up to strange dogs to stroke them in case they bite. A handicapping phobia can develop out of an uncontrolled incident with a boisterous dog, which can be very alarming if the child is not helped to get over it.

Insects and snakes provide another area of fear, and these may persist into adult life. Wasps and flies can be a focus in the summer, with whole families galvanized into action to beat them away at the picnic table. Various creepy-crawlies may induce hysterics in a normally calm and happy child.

Very loud noises also induce fears. Traffic noise, thunder, trains or the vacuum cleaner can induce terror in your toddler. Many a mother may have to leave vacuuming until her child is asleep or away playing.

Victoria, at two years old, suddenly became terrified of masks. This fear had originated in the swimming pool, when an exceptionally large boy had lounged in the babies' pool wearing goggles. Her panic at seeing him had rapidly generalized to masks within a couple of weeks. When visiting another child's house the sight of a mask would reduce her to a shrieking and clinging baby. Even two months after the visit she would ask about the mask if another trip was proposed.

The local toy shop had a large delivery of masks a couple of months later, and the stand was next to the entrance. It took her several weeks to face going into the toy shop past this stand. She would sidle by, hanging on to her mother's coat and then rush off into the back of the shop. It astonished her mother that the fear was so intense that toy shop visits were refused! During the following few months the avoidance was accepted by her mother, with occasional comments that the masks were funny and would not hurt her. Eventually Hallowe'en was approaching, and the play group was due to make some masks for an activity. It was planned to keep her away for those sessions, but for the preceding four weeks a local Woolworths also had a new display of masks.

Victoria then put herself through a desensitization to her fear. Of her own volition she approached the masks more closely on successive visits until she was able to go up and touch one. On shopping expeditions, she would rush in and go directly to the masks to test herself.

Eventually she picked one up, and on the next visit she looked through it and finally asked her mother to look through it. When asked if she would like to have one she refused, but remained fascinated by them.

A gamble was then made on letting her attend the play school session at Hallowe'en, hoping that the more boisterous boys would not put on their masks and deliberately set out to frighten each other. As luck would have it, it was a great success. She made a mask to take home, and wore it around the house to make her parents laugh. The next day she insisted on making another, and it was considered that her phobia was cured.

Sometimes it seems that your child has become unreasonably frightened after a relatively small incident, which then grows into a distressing and disturbing reaction. It may be that your child was feeling tired or particularly vulnerable that day, or that she suddenly becomes uncertain that you could protect her from the incident. It is not always easy to understand how your child felt on the frightening occasions, but her later reactions will indicate the intensity of her fear.

Teasing is a damaging way of reacting to your child's fear. Making fun of a trivial incident can be hurtful and worrying to your child, particularly if she is haunted by it. She may then try to keep her feelings inside, the problem will last longer, and it will not be so accessible to help or change at a later stage.

Ways in which you can help

1. Always accept your child's fears rather than disregarding or laughing at them. They are real to her, and your protection and sympathy is important to her.

2. Try a gentle and non-threatening approach to the feared object, reassuring and calming your child all the time.

3. Stop if she starts to get frightened. Don't force contact with the feared object, or you could produce a full-blown panic.

4. If the fear is more uncertainty and caution then encourage a gradual approach, ensuring that your child's fears do not

increase. Cuddle her or hold hands until she overcomes her slight fear.

5. If the fear is intense, avoid the object or the place. Only attempt a gradual approach when your child is feeling happy and relaxed. Perhaps give her a little snack as a treat, in order to distract her and amuse her while you try to get her closer to her feared object. The aim is never to increase her anxiety but to enable her to feel happy and calm while touching the frightening object.

6. Give your child some control over the situation so that she can get away if she wants to or approach on her own terms. Some fears are not important to face if they don't affect the normal running of life. You may choose just to let the normal course of events run, knowing that your child will probably eventually face up to the problem and overcome it herself. But other fears interrupt normal routines and have to be managed.

7. Try to identify what it is that is frightening and make a list, beginning with the least frightening aspect and leading up to the most frightening. A small dog fifty yards away on a lead is much less frightening than an unleashed alsatian bounding towards you and barking. Make the steps between the different stages small, so that your child cannot experience fear if you progress slowly enough.[4]

Tom, aged eighteen months, had been terrified of having a bath since his second week of life. His mother suspected that he had been dropped in the bath by the nursery nurse in the maternity hospital, as it was evident to her the first time he had become frightened of water.

Since that time she had given up trying to bath him, but had washed him with a flannel. Hair-washing was extremely difficult, and it needed both herself and her husband to cope with a screaming and kicking toddler.

Tom was generally happy to play with water but when it was related to bathrooms and washing he became resistant.

The first step was to get him used to going in the bath

without water. His mother did this by putting some of his favourite toys in the bath where he couldn't reach them, and lifting him in fully clothed to fetch them. When he was happy to get into the bath she started standing him in it while she washed his face and hands using water from the sink. Clothes were gradually removed and a non-slip mat put in the bath. When he was able to stand in it with no clothes on, a small amount of water was put in so that he could stand and splash in it. He still refused to sit down, so small toys were deliberately dropped in so that he had to bend down to pick them up. Washing him standing up, using the bath water, was then started, and the quantity of water was gradually increased.

At this point the problem was seen as resolved, even though Tom still preferred to stand rather than sit in the water. The final stages were left to natural progression and experience.

Hair-washing was introduced at bath time once he was happy with the bath. Games of showers, fountains and squirting were great fun, and he accepted getting his hair wet. When shampoo was introduced he wanted to do it himself and so was allowed to. Washing off the suds was achieved initially with a jet from a washing-up liquid bottle and eventually with a shower attachment.

Fear of the dark

Fear of the dark and of monsters is another very common childhood experience. Many parents accept this as totally normal, and just keep the lights on at night or provide a special night-light. One of us remembers her own childhood experience of being read *Ali Baba and the Forty Thieves*, and being terrified that night of someone coming to cut her up and put her into a large pot. She stifled under the bedclothes for many a night, terrified to look out in the dark, until her parents bought a pink night-light for her bedside table.

This fear is frequent in the school-age child but sometimes occurs with the preschooler. Parents may be confused at times whether the problem is one of going to bed or sleeping difficulties rather than a fear (see our companion volume, *My Child Won't Sleep*). Often the results are similar in that your child cries out for company or refuses to fall asleep on her own. If you are confident that your night-time management is good, but your child shows a specific reaction when you turn off the light, then it may well be a specific fear.

Some children link this to their strong imagination about monsters lurking in their rooms, and may involve parents in a complex ritual at bedtime, checking under the bed and in cupboards and drawers to see that there is nothing there. Story books and television programmes can disturb your child's fantasy so that they start to frighten themselves.

Sue at three years would play games during the day about monsters coming to catch her, and would delightedly run to her mother for protection. When she realized that she was starting to frighten herself she would turn the monster into a baby and pretend to go and pick it up to look after it, or she would start to say it was a friendly monster. Her control over her own imagination was sufficient to avoid scaring herself.

When books, pantomimes or television provide an addition to the child's natural fantasy there can be a dramatic increase in the level of fear that is outside the child's control.

The feeling of control is very important in managing fear, and many studies are now looking at the statements children make to themselves when coping with fear.[5,6] With the older preschooler it is possible to use these approaches and encourage your child to say that she feels brave and can manage the problem. Identifying the ways in which she can master the problem will help. If you don't admit her fear, or say that there is nothing to be frightened of, then she is not likely to feel helped. You are denying her feelings, you are not helping; she needs you to recognize them before she can overcome them.

Although the younger child cannot often say these things to herself, it may be helpful if you are able to say them for her.

Pointing out the fact that she can still call for you and you can hear her even though it is dark may help. Perhaps switching off the light and talking about where her toys and furniture are in her room is another way of helping her realize that the world doesn't change in the dark.[7]

The use of night-lights or leaving on landing lights is very frequent, and if your child shows fear of the dark then this may be a very reasonable way out. It doesn't overcome the fear but avoids it.

The sudden transition from summer time to winter time at certain phases of your child's development can also create some uncertainty about the darkness

> Linda was two and a half years old as winter time approached. She had become used to the light summer evenings and had little memorable experience of darkness as she was a good sleeper. Her parents recounted her first reaction to real darkness, which occurred when she was on a night-time car journey and asked them where the end of the tunnel was. She then demanded that the lights be turned on outside as she couldn't understand why it was dark.
>
> Soon after this she woke in the night crying that she couldn't see. Her parents decided to leave her dimmer light on low at night to reassure her if she did wake. They felt that her reaction wasn't so much fear as annoyance at not being able to see the things in her room when they put her to bed at night.

Fear of doctors and dentists

You may well have heard the advice that 'you overcome your own fear of the dentist when you have a child'. Many a parent will have posed calmly in the dentist's chair, smiling and reassuring their toddler.[8]

Dentists generally have a policy of encouraging children from the age of two years to go to the surgery to get to know the place and their dentist. They have a go with the equipment and may even open their mouths just to let the dentist have a look. Sometimes uncertainty about men may affect some preschoolers who have little male contact, and so the dentist or doctor is just another strange man. If you are frightened of the dentist yourself then it is not wise to have your child in with you while you have treatment. No matter how you cover up your anxiety, your child will sense something and become uncertain. Also the prospect of seeing a strange man peer in her mother's mouth with a buzzing drill can be daunting.

Experience of a non-threatening form is important, and if your child does need to let the dentist probe in her mouth then there is often a special badge or sticker as a reward to look forward to.

If your child has developed a fear already then it will be helpful to make several trips to the surgery when nothing is to be done so that no anxiety is created. *Never* pretend that there will be no treatment if it is likely to be necessary, in the hope of forestalling a fearful reaction. It will only make your child feel mistrustful and more fearful of going again. She will not believe you again and the problems next time will be much worse.

With the older preschool child some information about the treatment will be helpful, to give them some anticipation and understanding of what is to happen. Pitch your information at a level your child can understand, and don't go into elaborate or gory details.

Doctors may not be so frightening a prospect to a preschooler, as visits with Mum to the surgery may well have occurred without any contact with the doctor. Many children don't like having their ears and throats examined, and the stethoscopes can be worrying. Practice at home on dolls and with toy stethoscopes can be a preparation for the general procedures. The elaborate games of doctors and nurses are usually games for the school-age rather than the preschool child. If your child has to go into hospital then refer to Chapter 7, where we discuss preparation for admission and separation from you.

Some children with long-term illnesses become very frightened of injections, to the extent that it interferes with their treatment.

Liza, a four-year-old, had an illness that necessitated a small blood sample every month. This involved a small finger prick and then smearing the drop of blood on to a card. Liza had become so frightened of this event that both of her parents had to hold her down screaming to prick her finger. This was very distressing to the whole family.

We planned a gradual stepwise programme over the next four weeks to reduce her anxiety.

(i) To leave the small needle in its sealed packet, and the card in the kitchen so she could see it every time she went in, and encourage her to pick them up if she wanted to.

(ii) To leave the needle packet open and encourage touching.

(iii) To leave the exposed needle out and supervise her holding it every day.

(iv) To have pretend trials of a finger prick and only hold the needle on her finger.

(v) To continue the pretend trials but to say that it was actually going to happen, but then not do it. This allowed an increase in her anxiety which rapidly went away when she realized it wasn't happening.

(vi) To repeat as above but actually to prick her finger after first warning her.

Liza passed through these different steps very successfully in the four weeks, and when her mother finally did the finger prick she said that it had hurt and cried a little but there was no panic or severe distress as there had been on previous occasions.

The opportunity for familiarity with feared objects, people and places when the child is happy and calm is the main goal to help overcome fear. It is very easy to absorb your child's fear yourself and studiously avoid any possibility of upsetting your child, but to continue this indefinitely will never allow your child to test out her reactions as she grows older, and it won't allow you to know that your child has resolved the problem.

Chapter 9
How do I teach sharing?

Sharing in the family

The family provides the main opportunity to learn to live cooperatively with others and you are responsible for teaching this to your children. With the first child, the process of sharing is directly with the parents, while with successive children this problem is roused repeatedly all through the day as each child asserts priority and ownership.

New parents have to learn how to share each other with the new baby and also share the baby. Some mothers become intricately bound up with the baby to the exclusion of their husbands, and this can cause the husband to have hurt feelings of rejection. Both need to be able to discuss this, try to understand each others' needs and reach a compromise that satisfies both sides. This experience can be a very helpful insight into the intensity of feelings evoked in a child when he has to share his parents with a new baby.

Sharing of attention and time is a vital part of family life. Every member has their individual need for attention from other members, and an intricate balancing act is often required. The new mother has to learn how to pay attention to her husband when he comes in from work in the evening, but equally the husband has to learn that his wife cannot provide the undivided attention that he had in their newly married days. She also needs recognition as a wife and a woman, not just as a mother. Sometimes husbands who focus too much on the child can engender feelings of being deserted and taken for granted in their wives. The process of re-adjustment and re-allocation of time and attention is a tender and sometimes volatile area.

Teaching sharing to your baby

The one-year-old still thinks that everything belongs to him, and that includes all of you as well. Distinctions between what is mummy's, daddy's and baby's are often stated by parents at this stage, and even though your child is only just starting to talk, he can understand much more than he can say. As he grows into his second year, there is more opportunity to demonstrate sharing to your child. Although it is still early to be able to expect your child to understand this as a concept, your demonstrations and examples will all contribute to his eventual understanding and ability to share. Sharing food from your plate, or splitting up a biscuit, provide basic simple examples.

'Mine' or 'me' are often among the first words that a child uses, and personal possession can be a very important feeling to a child. This is likely to develop from the parents' choice of words, and if they describe objects aggressively as 'mine' then their child is likely to do this as well. If the phrase 'This is daddy's sock' is used rather than 'That's mine' then your child is not likely to be so aggressively possessive.

The first child is often given in to a lot by his parents and so possession may not be such an issue. He may passively accept other young children taking his toys from his hands, as he is not used to fighting to protect his things. There will have been no adult example of protecting possessions, as many parents use avoidance tactics and just put precious or dangerous objects up out of reach so that battles are avoided.

This phase quite rapidly passes, as contact increases with other children and your child sees his favourite teddy being cuddled by another child. The most intense reactions of possession may be triggered by feeling tired, ill or uncertain, and your child just wants his normal security of you and his familiar toys. Another child disturbing this can set off a great rage in your child and he may not allow the other child to play or touch any of the toys.

The important part of this early stage of development is your continual demonstration of sharing. When you have sweets or biscuits you should share them with your child or ask if he would like one; if he has some then he may offer one to you or rapidly respond to a little suggestion of sharing. A two-year-old will be able voluntarily to share food even though a bag of crisps is his favourite thing to eat.[1]

Taking turns

Cooperative play develops gradually during the first and second year. The cooperative use of toys, for example, rolling a ball to each other, will occur at the end of the first year, and by the middle of the second year there is a change of interest from toys to the other child. Toys will be shared and given to each other, and as language progresses there is more play coopera- tion. One child will make a play suggestion that the other will follow. They will pretend to give each other food and drink or pretend to be different characters. Taking turns is clearly part of this process. Once your two-year-old is romping around shouting 'Come on, let's go upstairs' to his friend then you know that taking turns can now be included in play.

Beth and Sue at two years of age would take turns in giving each other a push round in a rotating armchair. Sometimes the one who was having the ride would decide it was time to change over and sometimes the pusher would choose to change. As both were lively only children, they balanced their turns well without either being dominant, and with- out adult interference.

It is difficult for a child to learn to wait his turn beyond one other child. Play in groups usually occurs in the fourth year, and then organized games that involve more than two chil- dren are more likely. The preschool child finds difficulty in maintaining contact with more than one child at a time, and so the more formal organized games with rules are not likely to be successful, particularly when turn-taking is involved. Group activities of singing nursery rhymes and dancing, for example, 'Ring a ring of roses' are possible, but 'The farmer in his den' is much more appropriate to the infant school.[2,3,4]

The preschool child will enjoy simple games of 'Snap' with an adult, but 'Happy families', which involves three or four people, is beyond him.

Problems with sharing

Nearly all parents at some time have to face pulling apart two children fighting over the same toy. Whether they be brother and sister or friends, the anger and frustration felt by both children is very intense. Some parents are embarrassed by this and don't like to see such possessiveness in their children. Several techniques are possible to solve the problem:[5]

1. If neither will give up and you don't know who had the toy first, then take it away from both of them and involve them with another activity.

2. If you know that one child grabbed the toy from the other, then grabbing is the problem. The toy should be given for a short while to the child who first had it, and then he should be encouraged to give it to the other child, who would like a go with it. Grabbing should not have a positive result, but teaching to ask and waiting should be rewarded.

3. If there is no possibility of the owner relinquishing the toy, then distracting the other child with a similar or better toy can solve the competition.

4. If one child has a clear emotional attachment to the toy, for example, a special doll or teddy, then the other child should always give it up even though he had first rights to it. This should be explained as his friend's 'special' toy, and another interesting activity can be introduced while congratulating and praising him on having given it back.

Sometimes parents become too involved in their children's fights over possession, particularly between brothers and sisters. Often it is wise to keep quiet and let them sort it out unless one child is regularly and unfairly dominating the other.

The older preschool child may have considerable battles about his toys with younger siblings, and it may be appropriate to keep certain special and fragile toys out of the way of the younger ones. A particular point can be made that the younger ones must not touch them, just as the parent safeguards her own precious possessions.

The balance between ages needs to be watched, as the older child can sometimes be bullied by a younger active sibling because he has been taught not to fight the smaller child. The rights of both age groups need to be recognized. The older one needs to see that the younger one is not as strong and does not understand so much, but he still needs to be allowed openly to claim back objects that he wants himself. If he is always told to give way to the young child he is likely to get his own way in a more sneaky and underhand manner.

Chapter 10

How do I cope with having another baby?

When is the right time to introduce another baby into the family? How can I make sure my children get on together? There are no easy answers to questions like these about brothers and sisters (siblings). Parents want their children to love each other and get on well, but they know that this doesn't always happen and that often there is fighting and jealousy. Sometimes marked differences in temperament, interests or age produce indifference or quarrelling between siblings, but as parents you can do some things which help children to get on together.

It is well known that young children can react very strongly to the birth of a brother or sister. In one study which looked at the reactions of young children to the birth of a brother or sister, the following were described soon after the birth.[1] Nearly all the children became more naughty and demanding, especially with their mothers, and over half were more clinging and tearful. A quarter had sleeping problems and many showed open jealousy and teased or irritated the baby. Wanting to be like the baby was also common, for instance using baby talk, wanting to be carried or fed like a baby, or a relapse in toilet training. Some children became more withdrawn. Difficult behaviour was more common in children who had volatile, negative moods, and where the mother was particularly tired or depressed after the birth.

On the other hand, half the children also showed surprising strides in independence. They began to feed, toilet or dress themselves, and some gave up the bottle. Most of the children were interested in the baby and affectionate to him and wanted to help in looking after him. So there were positive aspects in the children's responses to the baby as well as negative ones.

Preparing your child for the new baby

Preparing your child for a new birth is important, but it is impossible for her to imagine what it will be like when the new baby actually arrives.

Some parents leave discussion about the new baby until late in the pregnancy, as the time factor of waiting for the birth is too long for the two-year-old to understand. Other parents talk about it throughout the pregnancy and will repeatedly show the child pictures of when they were a baby and talk about what they used to do. It is difficult for your two-year-old not to know that something is different, and if you are trying to keep it a secret then this is likely to cause more unease. You cannot avoid meeting other mothers in the street and the occasional comments about the expected 'new arrival'. It is much better that your child knows from you about the new baby rather than someone else suddenly asking 'Are you looking forward to having a new baby sister or brother?'

There are many children's books about a new baby. Some even include the feelings of jealousy that can arise, and these are useful to have around before and after the birth. Discussions do not stop at the birth but need to continue afterwards, as your child is then experiencing the reality of having a baby around and may not like it even though she was prepared.

She may welcome him with open arms and then find that because her life is disrupted and she has less attention than before she is not so keen on the new arrival. For girls the disruption seems to be greatest if they have had a very close relationship with their mothers previously. When girls or boys have close relationships with their father they seem to get less upset, and his interest is very important to them. We have no evidence about this, but perhaps in general when children have close relationships with other people besides the mother they are less likely to feel left out when the baby comes along. Even if your child does become upset after the birth the chances are that this will clear up over the next year.

Some children are both caring *and* aggressive to their baby brother or sister. If you can promote the caring side and pay more attention to this aspect and not get too angry about the aggression, this will help.

It is important for you to provide positive comments to your older child about how to handle the new baby. 'Touch or kiss gently' is much better than 'Don't hurt him'. You need to indicate to your child how to behave rather than how not to behave. But don't be too easy-going about allowing your child too much freedom with the baby. Walking around carrying the baby is not really appropriate for a three-year-old, but sitting down securely with the baby on her lap under mum's supervision is fine. Some parents find it difficult to acknowledge that the older child is showing signs of aggression or anger towards the baby, while others are too careful or worried. There is a middle path you can adopt to the way your child is reacting to help her through a difficult phase. She needs to feel secure in your love and attention, but limits need to be set on how she is allowed to touch and handle the baby. Your guidance is part of her learning and is needed in the same way as when you help your child to approach a pet. You show her how to treat and hold the arrival without hurting and squeezing.

Involve your toddler as much as you can with the new baby, allowing her where possible to help, pointing out similarities between the baby and the toddler, and talking to the baby as though he were a person – these approaches appear to promote positive warm feelings between the two children, perhaps because they model their behaviour on yours, perhaps because it helps them to understand each other's needs better.[1]

Laura was two and a half when her baby brother was born. Her mother prepared her well for the event from the fourth month of pregnancy, talking about the baby in her tummy, and letting Laura touch her. Laura decided also to have a baby in her tummy, and her daddy had to feel it every morning before he went to work. When her mother went for her antenatal checks Laura also lay down for the doctor to feel her tummy.

After the birth Laura was very excited and happy. Her

mother made her a crib, and she had a new doll when the baby was brought home and was encouraged to imitate her mother looking after the baby. She showed no signs of aggression or anger towards the baby but became more clinging and attached to her mother. She had separated easily from her mother and had previously been to stay with her grandparents for a week, but after the birth was very reluctant to separate and could not be left at play school three months later. Laura still continues to have her baby in her tummy six months after the birth, although the regularity of the comments has become less.

Not surprisingly, women get very tired and often feel depressed during the first few weeks of a baby's life, and find it hard to cope with the demands of the baby and a toddler. This is the time when help from husbands, friends and relatives can be vital. They can make sure that the mother has sufficient rest and can give to the toddler the attention and care she is used to so that she does not feel left out. It is a great help if this care can be provided by someone who knows the toddler well, so there is the least disruption of her routine. The less her life is disrupted the easier it will be for her to cope.

Bathing and feeding the baby are the times when a toddler is most likely to feel left out and become interfering and irritating. Once you start feeding you can't really stop, so make good preparation before these times with games and toys at hand, and be ready to respond to her demands or involve her with care of the baby, and she will not feel so excluded or upset. Many mothers rapidly learn to have books and a potty beside them when they sit down to feed the new baby, as their older child is likely to demand attention just at that time.

Linda at two and a half would become extremely noisy whenever her mother began to breastfeed the new baby. She would rush about shouting and singing and banging her toys, and was at times extremely disruptive.

Jealousy

Jealousy of a new baby is influenced by many factors. It is a very complex emotion, and can, for instance, be combined with warm protective feelings. Attitudes to the baby depend to some extent on a toddler's relationship with her parents before the birth. If there were many conflicts prior to the birth she is likely to develop a teasing attitude to the baby.

It may be a long while before the eldest child has the ability to express her feelings of jealousy in words.

Christopher was five when his second younger sister was born. As his mother was talking to the middle child, aged two, about the new baby he was able to say 'I know how Sarah feels.' His mother was surprised at this sudden revelation, as he had never mentioned his upset feelings when Sarah was born even though he had been given plenty of opportunity.

A child with a difficult temperament who cannot adapt to new situations and has a negative approach will find it harder to adjust to a different family situation. On the other hand, the availability of other supports for your toddler and your efforts to involve her with the baby can help to promote pleasant feelings towards the baby.

Sometimes parents prefer one child to the other, and this may reinforce jealousy that is already there or cause it to develop. It is never easy to know how these preferences develop. Your child may have a difficult personality and jealousy may be added to other difficulties because you prefer (or she thinks you prefer) the other, easier child. You may actually begin to prefer one child because you don't like the jealousy shown by the other. Some parents show a sex preference for their children, with either the boy or girl being a favourite. It is painful for parents to find they prefer one of their children to the others, or to be accused of not loving a child when they feel they have been giving equally to all. Unknowingly you may be showing preference to one child which your other child inevitably notices. If one child is difficult or naughty it is worth thinking whether there are any differences in your behaviour towards the children.

Margaret, aged four, was disagreeable to other children and adults, and teased her younger brother James a great deal, often giving him a push or hit when no one was looking. James was naughty too, but his mother laughed at his naughtiness whereas she always told off Margaret when she was doing something wrong. Margaret tried hard to attract her mother's attention, but she could never arouse her mother's warmth and interest as James could.

Margaret's mother was not aware of how different her responses were to the two children. She decided to try to be much more positive to Margaret, to notice the good things she did and to stop comparing the two children. Her changed behaviour did have some effect on Margaret, who seemed to feel more loved and could enjoy herself more, and was then nicer to other people, including James.

Naturally everyone makes a fuss of a new baby when they first visit. It can be very painful for your toddler when a previously doting granny suddenly ignores her. If your visitors are not sensitive to her needs you will have to make extra efforts to make sure she is not left out.

Sometimes grandparents like one child more than another. This can create a lot of tension, as you don't want to quarrel with them or deprive your other child of their affection. Your response will have to depend on how your children are affected and whether one child is becoming very upset.

Should I treat my children exactly the same?

Parents often wonder whether they should treat their children exactly the same, especially if they are close together in age. Some parents never give anything to one child without giving to the other, and even try to dress them the same. Other parents make a determined effort to treat each child differently. It is probably true that however hard you try you can't treat two children the same, because they are likely to have different personalities and respond differently to your behaviour. You may need to be firmer, or more patient, or more pushing with one child than with another. One child may need little sleep, and another may get very irritable if she has less than nine hours.

Also, the circumstances surrounding each child's experience as she grows up are very different. The first child often has her parent's individual attention until the second child arrives, and the second child never has this same early experience and opportunity.

Mrs Brown noticed that when her third child was born he had to wait for his feeds and attention while she dealt with the older two children. Mark began to wake more at night. His mother felt that he had developed this pattern because night-time was the one time when he would not be interrupted or delayed in his demands. She had not experienced sleeping difficulties with either of the other two children.

Parents may expect that the second child can re-use the clothes, toys and equipment that the first child has grown out of. You may be surprised to find intense feelings of possession developing in the first-born towards her high chair or buggy, which exclude the new baby from using them. Some mothers just buy another high chair to overcome the problem and prevent jealousy. These difficulties are more likely to occur over items that the first child remembers well, and also if the ages of the children are close, so that there is competition to be a baby.

There can be no hard and fast rule about whether you should treat your children the same. It is often appropriate for an older child to have some privileges, for instance going to bed a bit later, going out to friends on her own. It is important to provide opportunities for both children to have areas of independence from you, but then they will both want to be babied at other times. This change in need will vary according to how they feel, illness, and the different stresses on them, such as starting school. Every child fluctuates between wanting to grow up and wanting to be like a baby, and forcing them either way is likely to cause difficulties later on. An elder child should not be kept at the level of the younger child, but neither should she grow up too fast and take on too much responsibility. She exists in her own right and is not just an adjunct of her brother or sister.

It is unlikely that boys and girls in the same family will be treated the same. Attitudes and expectations are very different for sons and daughters; even from birth they are played with differently, given different toys, expected to do different things. It doesn't necessarily follow that boys are *preferred* to girls because they are treated differently, although in many cultures daughters are certainly valued less than sons. In our society there are probably wide differences in parents' attitudes; some don't mind what sex their children are, others have strong preferences. If you aren't aware of your preferences you may not realize how differently you are behaving to the boys and girls in your family.

A major difficulty faced by some parents is knowing how to ensure fairness when one child is handicapped. You don't want your handicapped child to suffer and yet she may be unable to do many of the things that other children do. On the other hand you don't want your healthy child to sacrifice too much for her handicapped sister or brother. You have to work out a compromise for your family, but it is important to try and keep all the children's needs in mind.

Chapter 11
How do I cope with feeding?

Feeding problems are a major cause of worry to parents. It is terrible to think that your child is not getting enough to eat, and it is only too easy to battle every meal-time trying to force your child to eat more. You find you cannot *make* your child eat, and he readily learns how worked up you become when he teases you by refusing food.

These problems are common.[1] Very poor appetite was described in 16 per cent of a group of three-year-olds, and over 11 per cent had marked food fads or finickiness and chose to eat a very limited diet.[2]

The first year

Difficulties over eating in the toddler may stem from problems in the first year, although very often they occur in children who formerly ate well.

Most babies feed poorly at one time or another and parental anxiety may exaggerate the severity of the problem. Breastfeeding is a particular source of worry because it is so difficult to know how much milk a child has taken at a feed. One of the commonest causes for stopping breastfeeding is anxiety that a child is not having enough to eat.[3] Breastfed babies often cry a lot in the evening, and this makes parents feel that breast milk is inadequate. Demand feeding, especially in the first three months, might reduce the evening crying and help you to feel confident that your child is getting enough to eat.

As long as your child gains weight the food intake is sufficient. In the first few weeks weight gain may be slow until your baby is sucking well and the milk flow is well established. There are some babies who do not gain weight, and if this happens to your child you will obviously want to seek advice and try to sort it out.

Babies often posset food. They bring up a little of what they have just eaten and seem to like the taste of the milk curds in their mouths. Occasionally they may bring back most of the food you have just given them. This may be due to wind or having eaten too much or too quickly. If it happens regularly you may have to consult your doctor.

Introducing solids

By about three months babies are able to coordinate their tongue and other muscles so that they can swallow food. The age at which solids are introduced varies with fashion, and some babies seem to need them earlier than others. A sudden increase in demand feeding or a shortening of time between feeds can be an indication that your child is not getting enough and would benefit from solids. It is probably a good idea to start introducing your child to solid food fairly early on – at least by five months. You will not feel pressurized then, and he will have plenty of opportunity to try a teaspoon at a time of many different flavours. If he gets frantic with hunger you could give him a new solid just after he has got over his most acute hunger by drinking some milk, and he should be more receptive then. Some people find it better to give the solids first before the baby is filled up with milk. By the time you are wanting him to have solids more regularly he should be accustomed to various foods and accept them happily. If you don't introduce solids earlier, you may find at eight or nine months that your child rejects all attempts to give them to him. Many nine- to ten-month-olds will happily hold a biscuit or banana and eat it, although they reject all attempts to spoonfeed them and spit out the lumps.

Changing from breast and bottle to cup

Some mothers choose to move from the breast to a special bottle with a teat more like a nipple than the ordinary bottle, while others move straight from the breast to a bottle or a cup. By about six to eight months a baby can be drinking from a teacher-beaker. Some parents find that it is easier to wean suddenly from breast to bottle or bottle to beaker. Most feel that the gradual introduction of something new is easier, for example, replacing one feed a day by the new method or using the new bottle or feeder at the end of a feed.

The longer you continue breast or bottle feeding the harder it may be for your child to adapt to something new. If he has got used to having breast or bottle feeds at night it may be particularly difficult for him to change (see our companion volume, *My Child Won't Sleep*).

It is certainly worth thinking ahead from the early months about how you are going to introduce new feeding methods or solid foods. For instance, if you are planning to breastfeed for six or nine months it is worth giving your baby a bottle of milk every now and then. You can use your own expressed milk if you don't want to use milk powder. This means that the father can sometimes give a feed if the mother is tired at night or unavoidably delayed; it also allows your baby to grow accustomed to the bottle and be more ready to accept it. Similarly you can give your baby juice or water in a beaker as soon as he can take it, and this will smooth the way to changing over to a beaker completely.

Weaning

Weaning is often dreaded by parents. You have a well-established pattern of feeding, and you are reluctant to change it and face the prospect of your child being upset and not getting enough to eat. If you are breastfeeding you may be as reluctant to give up this close, enjoyable activity as your baby. Plenty of women do go on breastfeeding into their child's second year, and this is very much a personal decision. The time will come when you want to stop, and at this point it is sometimes difficult to know how to set about it.

Some babies voluntarily give up the breast or bottle, while with others a gradual process of weaning is necessary. Drop one feed at a time, starting with the one which is least important and keeping the ones which are important for comfort. If your baby will only fall asleep on the breast or bottle, now is the time to start thinking of putting him down while he is still awake. Practise by putting him in his cot awake after the midday meal, and encourage him to fall asleep without sucking (see *My Child Won't Sleep*).

The midday meal is often the easiest one at which to start the weaning process. Try giving solid foods first and then a drink in a beaker, and finally the breast. Your child should soon be able to give up the breast at this feed, and if he persists you may have to button up your clothes, distract him with a game and persist in your refusal. Babies can smell their mother's milk, so it can be tantalizing for them if you stay around, and easier if the father takes over.

The next feed to drop could be the tea-time one, followed perhaps by dropping the evening one (if you can get him to fall asleep without sucking) or the morning one. Some women prefer to make the early morning feed the last one to give up. In this way the breasts are emptied for the day, you can have a nice cuddle in bed and perhaps even another two hours' sleep before your child wakes for good.

Weaning can sometimes take a long time, but if you persist and gradually reduce the feeds you'll get there in the end. A period of about two to three months is the average, but if you take longer don't worry.[4]

Finger feeding

Your main aim is to make feeding a calm, pleasurable time. Once you begin to feel tense or anxious your child senses this. He is then likely to lose his appetite, be unwilling to try anything new or perhaps tease you by refusing your offers of food. Some infants find it hard to adapt to new things, new foods, new feeding methods, new textures. These infants need more opportunities to try things out and it requires a lot of patience to encourage them. Keep trying small steps at a time and he will eventually get used to these new situations.

A possible source of tension is when your child wants to start feeding himself from about six to seven months onwards.

He enjoys the experience of getting a biscuit or a piece of banana to his mouth and biting it (especially if he is teething), and the texture of the food in his mouth, but his coordination is poor and most of the food goes anywhere but in his mouth. Once he starts using a spoon, from about eleven months onwards, the mess will be even worse! If he is teething he can bite pieces off and you may get concerned about him choking. If you are worried about this, give him a type of biscuit that dissolves easily.

You may be a tidy person, and the mess produced by a fourteen-month-old can be quite revolting. Choose a high chair that is easily wipeable and put paper or plastic on the floor and you won't feel so upset. Bibs with sleeves or a tray can also be a help. Meals can take ages, but if you try to feed your son, he won't let you, and if he tries to feed himself he doesn't succeed or just plays around. After feeding him something yourself you may have to leave him to it, giving him foods which are reasonably easy to eat with his hands, or later with a spoon. It's worth being patient about this stage, so that by the time your child can feed himself properly he should associate food with pleasantness and fun, not with tension and being told off. Good table manners can always follow later!

Poor appetite

Poor appetite is often a worry to parents from the second or third year onwards. It is a common worry and is perhaps related to change in growth patterns. Children are still very active and still getting taller but the *rate* of gaining weight is definitely slowing down in the second year compared with the first year of life. The best way to see if your child is growing normally is to check his growth on a growth chart, which you should be able to get from your child health clinic (see Figure 3). Growth charts are based on studies of large numbers of children at different ages. They show that increase in weight and height is very rapid in the first year and then slows down. In Figure 3, the middle curve shows the average weight at each age, and the upper and lower curves show the range of normal

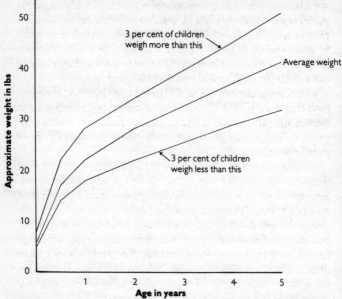

*Figure 3. A simplified diagram of weight gain
from 0–5 years*

weights that occur. As long as your child's rate of growth
follows the general trend there is unlikely to be anything
wrong with his growth. If he suddenly starts slowing down in
the rate of his growth that is a cause for worry. Gain in height
is a better indicator of normal growth than increasing weight;
a child who is gaining height normally is usually having an
adequate food intake.

So although you think your two-year-old has a poor appetite, he may be having an adequate food intake. It is at this
point that you find yourself entangled in an exhausting battle
over meals as you try to make your child eat more.

Sue, aged twenty-two months, had been a poor eater since
birth and her parents had always been worried about her
growth. She was at the lower end of the normal range for

weight and had put on weight slowly but regularly. Both parents hovered over her at meal-times, trying all sorts of tactics to get her to eat. They would threaten her, try to force food down her with a spoon, try to bribe her with sweets. Sue and her mother often ended up in tears, but Sue's eating did not improve. The following plan was developed:

(i) Very small portions of food were placed on Sue's plate four times a day and she was left completely on her own for fifteen minutes to eat it. If she ate the food she was briefly praised; if not it was taken away quietly and the whole matter was ignored.

(ii) The portions of food were gradually increased as Sue was able to clear her plate, but the question of eating and appetite was never discussed in her presence and the parents stopped trying to make her eat.

It was very difficult for Sue's parents to leave her alone, but they did find that they had been distracting her from eating by their presence and fussing. They had also found it difficult to allow her to try feeding herself because they were so worried she would not get enough, but once she got enjoyment doing this she began to eat more.

Brian was a boy of three and a half who had a very small appetite. He had no set meal-times and his mother would follow him around all day offering him food. He often had a bottle of milk in his mouth and he ate quite a lot of sweets and biscuits during the course of a day. He ate better at his nursery, where he was made to sit at the table with other children.

The programme decided on by the parents was to limit Brian's bottles of milk to four a day, after meal-times, and one at night when he woke, and the rest of the time to give him water in a cup if he was thirsty. Biscuits were limited to two immediately after lunch and supper, and sweets were given after tea, but only if he finished his meal. Meals were at set times and rigidly stuck to, and Brian was required to sit down at the table although no pressure was put on him to eat.

At first Brian objected strongly to this changed pattern, but as no notice was taken of his complaints he did begin to eat more regularly. It was also possible to change him over from using a bottle to using a drinking beaker, and eventually to stop the night-time bottle (see *My Child Won't Sleep*).

His grandparents gave him a lot of sweets when they visited and it was difficult for Brian's parents to influence this. They were helped when the grandparents went away for six weeks. When they came back Brian's improved eating was fairly well established.

Giving your child attention when he eats, and no attention if he is not eating, is not easy.[5] If you can carry this out you will prevent the establishment of a pattern where he becomes more interested in the attention he gets for *not* eating than in the food itself. In general, given the opportunity of a balanced diet, children will eat what they need. Sweets and biscuits are very filling, so if your child doesn't eat much cut these out. Sugar is addictive, and if you provide a lot of sugar-rich foods in their diet children will begin to choose these rather than other foods.

Parents often make eating into a game: 'One for teddy . . . one for you . . . one for mummy . . . one for you.' This can work successfully as long as it does not become an elaborate ritual and more exciting than eating. Playfulness is often a good way to smooth over times of difficulty.

Food fads

Some parents are very finicky about what they eat and will only eat a few sorts of foods or complain a lot about what they are offered. Children soon pick up adult attitudes, and if a parent or another child in the family is very fussy about what they eat a younger child can soon copy this. The opportunity to savour lots of different foods and textures in a relaxed atmosphere helps to promote flexible eating habits. But in spite of the varied experience many children develop food fads: for instance they occur in 11 per cent of three-year-olds.[2]

They develop strong dislikes of certain tastes or textures, won't chew meat or eat anything lumpy, perhaps refuse all meat or vegetables. It's very frustrating when well-cooked meals are refused and chips or cornflakes are requested yet again. It is not clear why children go through this stage. It is often associated with a preoccupation with cleanliness and order, and a time when children are concerned about their bodies and about elimination functions and what happens to food when it is eaten.

Discussion of these things at a simple level may help your child, but often you will just have to wait for him to grow out of it over the next few years. After all, beans and fish fingers make quite a balanced diet! All you can do is to offer your child as varied a diet as possible and insist he eats a bit of even the things he doesn't like, or substitute fruit for vegetables. Possibly you can make having his pudding dependent on eating some of the first course, although this isn't always successful.

As you will find out, a confrontation is doomed to failure because you can't make your child eat something he doesn't want to – he will just spit it out or even be sick.

Slow encouragement may be more successful.

Harry, aged four, refused to eat anything hard like carrots or apples and the dentist was worried about his teeth. It was decided that at every meal a small piece of carrot, apple or something else hard should be put on Harry's plate. If he ate it he was given a star on his star chart. His parents agreed to stop nagging him about his diet and were delighted when he began to chew all the hard things. Harry was pleased with his stars and was quite surprised to find he quite liked the new foods. From then on his diet gradually became more varied.

Strange foods

Young children tend to put anything interesting into their mouths when they start crawling. This can be quite a problem. They seem to delight in eating soil or plants, and coal was very popular when it was widely used. If your child has an adequate diet this phase should eventually stop, and all you need to do is see that anything poisonous or dangerous is well out of the way. If he continues to eat strange, unusual things, this may be because his diet is inadequate, because he is bored, or because he is doing it to get your attention. Giving more attention at other times may stop the habit.

Overweight

Whether you consider your child too fat or too thin depends on your opinion. A child who was heavy at birth is more likely to continue on the heavy side through childhood. Heavy weight is probably influenced both by inherited tendencies and by family patterns of eating.

Eating is a highly emotional subject, and some parents feel that by giving their child food they are proving their affection and care. The more their child eats the happier he makes his parent. Young children will probably stop feeding once they have had enough, but this biological response is overcome in some children who are persuaded to eat more and more as they grow older. Children who get into the habit of eating a lot may well come from families where this is the family pattern of eating, so it's worth thinking whether you really want your child to be as fat as you are!

Some children seem to eat a lot to comfort themselves or because they are bored. As adults we may eat a bar of chocolate when we are upset and this response may develop even in quite young children. They may be accused of stealing food from the fridge, or biscuits from the cupboard, and stuff themselves whenever they get the chance. Other children use demands for food and drink to get attention. They continually ask for something to eat or drink in order to attract attention, and when their demands are met they are encouraged to continue this behaviour.

Wayne, aged three and a half, felt that he was less favoured than his younger brother, who did indeed get more attention. Wayne was always looking for something to eat and would demolish a packet of biscuits if given a chance. He was frequently given sweets and cake to keep him quiet.

The parents agreed that Wayne probably felt left out since his brother had been born. They decided not to use food as a way of keeping Wayne quiet, but to limit the amount of biscuits and sweets he could have each day and to give these out at specified times. They also put aside definite times each day just for Wayne to be with them. If he demanded food at other times they tried to give him extra attention instead, and Wayne gradually began to demand less food.[6]

Food, especially sweets and biscuits, is used by parents as a way of keeping children quiet, as a reward, or to show affection. This will not matter as long as you keep it in proportion and remember that your attention and interest are more rewarding to your child than anything else. In this book we do sometimes suggest using sweets and biscuits as rewards for 'good' behaviour. You may decide you do not want to do this because it is bad for your child's teeth, will make him over-weight, or because he might get used to eating as a comfort and a way of relieving tension. This is a sensible approach. Occasionally it may be worth relaxing your rules if you are faced with a really difficult problem and cannot find any other good incentive for your child. Even if you do use sweets as a reward this should only be for a short period, and after a while it should be possible to reduce dependence on the reward as the difficult behaviour improves.

Chapter 12
How do I manage toilet training?

Most parents tend to start thinking about toilet training around the middle to end of their child's second year. Some like to start earlier, while other parents are not concerned and leave it until the child is about two years old. Washing machines, launderettes and disposable nappies have made the stress of a child in nappies much lighter, and often, therefore, mothers do not have a great incentive to get their children clean and dry. It is worth considering that there is some evidence that if you start toilet training before twenty months you are likely to be successful more quickly.[1]

Normal training methods[2]

Children are usually physically mature enough to hold their urine for between one and two hours without frequent leaks by about eighteen months, although there are large individual differences in this ability. A good indication of when they are ready to start potty training is when there are reliable and frequent periods of staying dry in nappies. It is easier to tell this if the child is in terry nappies rather than disposables. If once you change her you notice that she manages to stay dry for an hour or so, then this is an indication that she has some bladder control. Younger children pass urine very frequently and show no real ability to retain it.

You can buy a potty and have it around the house, telling your child what it is for and perhaps helping her hold her dolls on it to have a pretend wee. She may want to sit on it with her nappies on just to try it out. It is probably wise not to allow her to play with it, putting her toys in and out of it or wearing it on her head as this confuses its purpose.

The next stage is to encourage your child to sit on it at regular times during the day when she is most likely to want to wee. This is usually after meals or a drink. If she does manage to perform appropriately then show your delight so that she realizes what is expected of her.

Many parents find that even though they have introduced the potty and given all the indications of how to use it they cannot get their lively toddlers to sit down on it for more than half a second at a time. A phase of bobbing up and down is quite usual, when you may be able to encourage your toddler to sit on it but unfortunately not stay on it long enough to catch anything.

The only answer to this is to keep on trying, but not to get worked up about it. If it is convenient and about the right time of day to encourage an attempt to sit on it then have a go, but if it doesn't work then don't worry. The major feature about toilet training is to avoid getting upset or bothered about the whole issue. It will happen at some point, and if you tear your hair out on the way that won't speed it up. Often a turning point is the first time a wee actually gets into the potty and your child makes a realistic connection between the potty and her bodily functions. Unless this is just an early chance event you may now be on the way to a trained child.

Your child gradually learns how to control and release the muscles that let her wee. As soon as she has had a few successes in the potty and you decide to start training in earnest then day-time nappies should be discarded completely.

The actual phase of potty training may only last a few days if your child is ready.[3] The association between voluntarily passing urine and sitting on the potty is made quickly, and if you remember to regularly pot her then you will have very few accidents. In the first few weeks it depends on you to suggest using the potty regularly and at the right time. For a mother who has had a child in nappies for eighteen months this can be an additional responsibility that is occasionally forgotten. Your life starts to revolve around making it to the shops and back without an accident, and worrying about what happens if she wants to go while you are stuck at the checkout in Sainsbury's.

She will soon be able to warn you when she wants to wee, but the time delay will be very short. You need to move quickly at this stage once she has told you, and so a quick exit up a side street to hold her over the gutter is often the only recourse available. It is astonishing how difficult toilets are to find when you are in a hurry. Department stores tend to place them on the top floor in very inaccessible places. Even if you are lucky enough to have a cooperative child who performs in the potty before you go out shopping, you are likely to get caught short at some stage.

In these early stages of gaining muscle control your child is still likely to wet if she falls asleep during the day, so it is usually wise to put a nappy on her for day-time naps. The problem then comes when falling asleep in the car or in the buggy, when accidents can happen. It is tempting to put a nappy back on her at this stage, but it is difficult to know whether this will counter the training that has already been done. If your child does indicate that she wants a wee in the car and you have put a nappy on her then it is tempting to tell her that it's all right to do it in the nappy. If you are keen to keep the toilet training as fast and reliable as possible then you must not be lazy, but give the opportunity to use the potty whenever it is requested or at regular intervals. Some parents carry a potty around with the child whenever they go out for the first couple of months after training. There is a potty with a lid that is very useful for transporting, or for discreet dumping of contents!

Of course, the time of year is a very important factor in toilet training. It is much easier in the summer, when there are fewer clothes and your child is likely to be rushing around the garden or park with nothing on. The inconvenience of winter, when you have to muffle them up in snow suits, wellies and extra layers of clothes, operates against an easy or fast squat. One thing worth keeping in mind: if you are about to train your child in the winter then choose a duffle coat rather than an all-in-one snow suit as outer clothing, as it is much easier to unfasten in an emergency. The other useful tip is to choose dresses and tights for girls, as it is much easier than fiddling around with dungarees for this particular phase, and if you have a boy then choose dungarees that have very easy fastening or trousers with an elasticated waist that come down quickly. The intermittent and emergency wee phase tends to last a couple of months, and then you will gradually find that your child is able to hold on longer and longer.

It can be quite distressing four or five months later when you feel that all has gone well and then suddenly you find a puddle on the carpet. There are likely to be the occasional accidents and it is easy to feel cross when you know that your child can ask perfectly well. It may be associated with her feeling a bit ill or anxious, but is usually due to a lack of concentration. Your toddler becomes so engrossed in what she is doing that she completely forgets about her other end and suddenly finds a puddle. This can surprise her as much as it does you. If it starts to happen regularly then tighten up your toileting programme again and remind her more frequently, rather than just expecting her to tell you when she wants to go. Mothers can often tell when their child wants to wee well before she actually chooses to go. If the time delay is too long and she is not getting there in time any longer, then the occasional prompt from you can do no harm.

As a guideline to what you might expect, surveys have found that 60 per cent of children are dry by two and a half years and nearly 90 per cent by three years.

Learning normal bowel control

In most instances it is not necessary to make a special effort to achieve bowel training. Your child automatically learns to use the potty for doing a pooh while she is doing a wee. Some children separately indicate when they want to empty their bowels, and ask for the potty again within a few minutes of having sat down for a wee.

Babies in the first year cry when they have a soiled nappy and there is sometimes an intolerance to this, while wet nappies are a normal part of life. In the second year your child may ask to be changed as soon as she has emptied her bowels in her nappy, and if this occurs at a regular time of day you may be able to put her on the potty to catch the motion. This avoids dirty nappies for you, but is not real toilet training as it is totally dependent on you guessing the correct time to pot her.

With some children it becomes necessary to focus on bowel training as they are reluctant to use the potty for this although they will pass urine happily in the potty. Your child may have a phase of asking to have a nappy put on to do a pooh. Gentle suggestions and keeping calm will help this phase to pass.

Bowel training is an area of child-care that can induce a lot of strong feelings in adults, whether it be embarrassment or disgust. This is our problem not our children's. Elimination is a natural function that has to be controlled to be socially acceptable. It is important to be hygienic about toileting, but this does not mean we have to induce fear or disgust in our children. Toddlers are interested in what they have done in the potty, and although you can gently discourage them from touching it you should also be pleased and show some interest. Some parents feel it is important for children only to use the potty in the bathroom, while others allow their child to sit on it anywhere. Family complaints can start to limit this some-times, particularly when your child is about to have a bowel action while on the potty in the living-room in front of the television. For parents who don't mind where potties are used, a lot of energy can be saved by having one potty upstairs and another downstairs so that you don't have to keep rushing up and down to find it.

About 10 per cent of children are still soiling at three years, but by four years this has fallen to 3 per cent.

Training at night

Staying dry at night usually happens after staying dry in the day, although not always. Some children don't begin to achieve this until they are three years old. Again it will be your child who provides the indication that she is ready to leave off her night nappy. A series of dry nappies and an early morning call for a wee will indicate that she is able to control her bladder sufficiently well. Some children just suddenly tell their parents that they don't want to wear a nappy any more. Realizing that a friend is dry at night can provoke this, or a second baby in the family can make the older child want to feel different and more grown up. Obviously the converse can apply, and some children will revert to nappies for a short while on the arrival of a new member of the family.

One common method of encouraging dry beds is for parents to lift their child when they go to bed and take her to the toilet. This can help ensure a dry bed but does not really help your child's bladder control. She can come to rely on you doing this and the procedure can carry on for quite a long time. If you do decide to lift your child at night, then it is very important to make sure that you wake your child up so that she is fully aware of what is happening, otherwise she will continue to wet her bed when she is half awake.

The ultimate goal of full toilet training is for your child to be able to tell you or go to the toilet or potty by herself to do a wee and a pooh during the day and at night. The course of toilet training and its speed will mostly depend on you. If you are very keen to get your child out of nappies then you will probably start the whole procedure slightly too early for your child. This won't cause any harm but will only produce a lot more additional work for you. You will have to remember to pot her, as she will be too young to indicate on her own when she wants to go. If you start training at the time you feel your child is showing some bladder control then it will probably only take a few weeks, but if you start several months before this it will still be those several months before your child is physically mature enough to learn control.

The same applies to night-time training. If you are keen to remove nappies at night but have to keep lifting your child to ensure a dry bed then you are creating work for yourself. You may as well leave the nappies on until your child is able to wake herself up with the feeling of wanting to go to the toilet. Once she is doing this reasonably reliably then you can leave off the night nappy and just encourage her to call you or go on the potty on her own in her room.

Lapses in bladder control

Even though your child is reliably dry by day and night, there are likely to be the occasional wet pants or wet bed.[4] These instances can be caused by:

1. Stress and anxiety

A problem in the family, a change of house, a death, a birth, marital tiffs or upset, difficulties in parent/child relationships, can all be related to lapses in bladder control. Embarrassment can also be important. A child in unfamiliar surroundings may be frightened or embarrassed to ask an adult where the toilet is. Not having mum around with their own private communication system can cause a child to hang on too long. It is actually wise to choose a word for urinating that most people will understand, rather than a family nickname.

Staying in a strange house for the night may produce a wet bed, if your child is not sure where the toilet is or is frightened to get up in the middle of the night. Try to provide a potty in the room for occasions such as these.

2. Excitement and anticipation

All high emotional arousal states weaken bladder and bowel control: this is a natural bodily reaction. So your child may suddenly wet herself unexpectedly at a party or on an outing. Sometimes the planning and looking forward to the event will weaken bladder control at night, and parents who don't realize the connection may sadly cancel the anticipated event in anger at the lapse in control. Laziness is often cited in this type of case, rather than realizing the state of emotional excitement that children can reach. Reassurance and gentle reminders can often help over these difficulties; threats and anger will make the matter worse.

3. Illness

If your child is sickening for something then generally her level of capability falls and she requires much more parent contact and help. She often wants more cuddles, to be fed more baby-type food and may lapse in her toileting habits.

Sometimes a specific urinary infection can be the cause of sudden and repeated lapses of bladder control in the day and at night. This is quite common in girls. If your daughter is having to pass water frequently and complains of burning or pain when she does so, or gets sore, then you may suspect a urinary infection which will need checking with your general practitioner. An allergic reaction, sometimes to food, can produce a genital irritation and increasing frequency of passing water. Similarly, for bowel control, an adverse reaction to food will cause sudden diarrhoea that distresses everyone.

4. Fear

Occasionally, children suddenly become frightened of the toilet. This may be a generalized fear of being alone or may be a sudden onset after a frightening tale of being locked in alone from another child. An event may induce the fear, like the toilet seat falling on her, slipping in, or the toilet seat slipping while sitting on it. The occurrence of another frightening episode may be linked to it, like a wasp or spider being in the bathroom at the same time as the child. Once this fear has been detected (and it usually develops without your awareness), then you can implement tactics to defuse the problem. Going in with your child and giving her pleasant activities to do while sitting on the toilet can help overcome the fear and test out the reality that it is safe.

Occasional lapses of control are not to be worried about in the preschool child, although they can be irritating and annoying. If the lapse continues for some time and seems to be becoming entrenched, then it may be important to examine the reasons and approach your doctor or health clinic for advice.

Problems in toilet training

If your child has not achieved bowel control by about four years of age, bladder control by five years, or has been reliably toilet trained but shows significant and repetitive lapses of control, then it may be important to look more carefully at the reasons for this.[5]

1. Day-time enuresis or wetting

This includes any continual day-time wetting. In a survey of normal three-year-olds, it was found that 12 per cent of girls and 23 per cent of boys were still wetting once a week or more; by four most children are dry by day.[6] Boys tend to take longer to achieve full bladder control than girls and there is evidence that there are inherited tendencies to late bladder control.[7]

Things to do:

(i) Check that your child knows what to do when she has a full bladder.

(ii) Medical check for urinary infection.

(iii) Examine all the factors mentioned under lapses in bladder control, p. 118.

(iv) Try to remain relaxed about the problem and defuse any anxiety that you may be contributing to the situation.

(v) Show pleasure whenever your child uses the potty or toilet appropriately, but if there is a puddle say gently 'Never mind, let's try and get into the toilet next time.'

(vi) Sometimes a star chart, animal stickers or transfers can be given for managing to stay dry for a day or portion of the day. This needs to be linked with your praise and pleasure, as that is far more important than the sticker. No chart will work unless you participate in the sense of achievement that your child feels. Never take away a star once it has been earned. Try not to lose your temper if you can possibly avoid it.

Four-year-old Marianne wet during the day as well as at night. This was a great worry to her mother because a cousin of hers had also wet for many years and she was worried that Marianne was never going to be dry. Even after her urinary infections had been treated the wetting did not clear up. The parents nagged Marianne about her wetting and it was hard for them to feel optimistic about a toilet training programme; however, they agreed to the following programme:

(i) They would stop nagging Marianne because they could see that this just made her more hopeless about herself. They would not talk about wetting but praise her for being dry.

(ii) They would use a toilet training programme with her sitting on the toilet every two hours.

(iii) They would give Marianne a star for her chart if she was dry when they checked before she went to the toilet at the two-hourly intervals. Three stars meant a treat, a little toy or a walk or special game.

(iv) The intervals between going to the toilet were gradually lenthened as it became possible for Marianne to be dry. After a while the stars were given only if she was dry for half a day and then for a whole day. Gradually it was possible to fade out the stars and Marianne began going to the toilet on her own initiative.

2. Night-time enuresis or wetting

Your child may be well able to stay dry all day but will wet continuously or intermittently at night. The study of three-year-olds previously mentioned found that nearly a third of girls and nearly half of all boys of this age were wetting their beds at least once a week,[6] so don't worry too much about bed-wetting in the under-fives, your child may just be slower than average. Wetting tends to run in families, so if you have a family history of wetting at night your child, especially if he is a boy, may have inherited this tendency.

Things to do:

(i) Make sure you have a fitted waterproof undersheet on your child's bed.

(ii) If wet beds are getting you down then you can wake your child a couple of times in the night to get up and go to the toilet. Remember to wake her fully to do this.

(iii) Again try to keep calm and defuse any anxiety about wet beds. Reassure your child that everything is washable but show your pleasure at any dry beds that occur.

(iv) It is possible to try a deliberate teaching method in which you give your child a lot to drink before she goes to bed and then wake her several times during the night to go to the toilet. If she is able to stay dry with this method she should be well praised and encouraged to persevere. It gives your child a lot of opportunity to learn the right cues about bladder control and involves some intensive practice for a few nights.[8]

(v) Do not restrict fluids at bedtime, as this will not teach bladder control at all.

(vi) Some parents use what is called a 'bell and pad' or 'enuresis alarm'. This consists of a couple of wire mesh pads which are placed on the bed under the child's bottom, separated by a piece of sheeting with a normal sheet over the top. They are connected to an alarm box, and when your child wets the bed the alarm sounds immediately and wakes her up. It is then your job to get up and take her to the toilet, change the bed, and set the alarm again on the dry bed. The aim of the alarm is to wake the child just as soon as the first drops of urine occur, so that she wakes up and holds the rest until she gets to the toilet. It is unusual to use this method under the age of six, but if your child has been dry and has relapsed then you might want to try it.

It is wise to approach your doctor about this as many general practitioners' surgeries and health clinics have special 'enuresis clinics' for bed-wetters.

3. Encopresis or soiling

Some children never learn total bowel control while others may relapse after a period of control. This is usually quite a severe problem and your doctor's advice should be sought. Soiling is relatively uncommon, can occur during the day or at night and can involve just soiling pants or emptying the bowels in inappropriate and sometimes secret places. Smearing of the faeces sometimes occurs as well, but this is usually part of a wider behaviour problem.

Soiling can be caused by a wide range of problems, and is often linked with phases of constipation or holding on to bowel motions and stopping them coming out for as long as possible.

If you feel that your baby is constipated then it is very important to tell your doctor and obtain some laxatives in order to prevent a more severe problem later on. Some babies who have very hard faeces suffer pain when they empty their bowels. They then become frightened of the feeling and hold back their faeces, which makes the constipation and tummy-ache even worse. There can sometimes be a small cut in the lining of the rectum (an anal fissure), which also causes pain when the child defecates, and this can also lead to constipation and holding back of faeces. Your doctor will be able to examine for this.[9]

If your child is taking a long time to achieve bowel control, then set out a basic toilet training programme in which she sits on the potty or the toilet at regular intervals during the day, preferably after meals, and then reward any successful bowel movements with praise, stars on a chart or small surprises.[10] When she does it in her pants try not to appear upset, and ask her to try to do it in the toilet next time. Soiling is an unpleasant business, particularly when it's always up to you to do the clearing up. Make sure that you don't become entirely centred on her bottom in your contact with her, but make special times during the day when you can play together and have a pleasurable time. It is very easy to get wound up by soiling, and your life can seem to revolve around washing clothes and getting her to the toilet. Think what this does to her and make sure that she can get your attention in other ways as well. You deserve to enjoy your child, and she will be happy if you do.

With the older toddler who has managed normal bowel control, a sudden change to repeated soiling is an important indicator that there is something wrong. Emotional problems at home, either between parents or between parents and children, can lead to this particular behaviour problem, and professional advice should be requested.

Toilet training, like feeding problems, can really upset you. If your child isn't making as much progress as you would like, remember that it is rare for control not to develop. Bladder and bowel control will be achieved, but it will just take a bit longer than you expected.

Chapter 13
Summary

This final chapter summarizes our basic ideas on how to help your young child cope with the frustrations and challenges involved in growing up, how possibly to prevent behaviour difficulties from arising, and how to cope with them when they do occur.

The book is addressed to mothers and fathers, and we would like to stress how important it is for them to work together as a team. If a single parent or one member of a couple has responsibility for child-rearing, this can work out well, but if two parents are in disagreement this will inevitably lead to tension between them and make it more difficult for their child to know what they want, or to feel secure.

A lot of the book is written particularly for mothers because on the whole women are the ones who are mainly involved in child-care. This does not mean that we undervalue the importance of fathers' relationships with their children, or their capacities for giving love and care.

What can my child understand?

As a parent you are continually asking yourself: what does a one-year-old understand? How rational and sensible can you expect a two-year-old to be?

We have found that in making these decisions it is helpful for parents to think about what children can understand at different ages. If you over-estimate or under-estimate your child's understanding this can lead you into difficulties. Our experience is that parents often *under-estimate* their child's awareness of tensions and difficulties within the family, but *over-estimate* their abilities to understand reasoning.

Infants are very sensitive from birth to changes in the moods and feelings and behaviour of their parents, but their *under-*

standing about the causes of change and their ability to reason develops slowly.

Children are very likely to become upset if parents row, or if a parent gets depressed and stops paying them attention. From an early age they will be upset by the distress of adults or other children and try to comfort them. However, a two-year-old is not likely to be concerned about why you have to finish your dinner before you have your pudding, and you may waste a lot of energy if you try to reason about every issue, or expect 'rational' behaviour too soon.

Of course you don't think your six-month-old baby is naughty if he soils his nappy just after you have changed him, but some parents think their one-year-old is deliberately naughty if he drops his pudding on the floor. Some one-year-olds do realize what 'no' means, but they do not have a concept of right and wrong and are quite likely to respond playfully to 'no'. At about sixteen to eighteen months you can expect your child to respond regularly to 'no' by stopping what he is doing, but only when his language is well developed around the age of two and a half to three years can he really understand a simple *reason* for not doing something. At two to two and a half years he might understand 'Don't touch, it's hot.' At three to four years he begins to appreciate more complex reasons for doing things, like 'Clean your teeth so they will grow strong.' By all means discuss your reasoning and your ideas, but don't leave important decisions to him, for instance about whether he should wear a seat-belt, because he is not ready for that responsibility.

If you get into very complex discussions with your child about the rationale for doing something you are both likely to end up in a tangle. As likely as not he won't understand your reasoning, but he will see it as a good opportunity to enter into an argument. Sometimes after you have explained your reasons it may be better just to say 'Because I say so' rather than have an exhausting discussion. For instance, if you want to limit your child's intake of biscuits you say 'Three is the limit.' Your reasons might be: 'They are bad for your teeth', 'It will spoil your dinner', 'They will make you fat', 'It's expensive', 'Everyone has to have a share.' One reason should be enough! If you have a lot of reasons you won't sound very convincing, and further discussion will only lead your child to think you are indecisive. If he is going to persuade you to let him have more biscuits you might as well give in straight away.

Punishment

Parents often worry about punishing their children and especially about hitting them. It must be rare for a parent not to hit their child at some time. A quick slap certainly lets him know your opinion about what he is doing; a good hiding does the same, but is probably more of a relief to your feelings than a help to your child. If he is usually well-behaved, then probably another method of punishment would do just as well; if he is usually naughty, smacking probably has no effect at all.

Your love is more important than punishment in helping your child to be 'good'. As long as he feels safe and secure he will be ready to face the challenges of growing up and being independent. Learning to share and to cooperate will not be difficult for him if you have a happy relationship together and he knows he can depend on you.

A final few guidelines that we have found useful:

1. Don't under-estimate your child's sensitivity to emotions, but try also to match your expectations to his current level of development. If he is two and a half, don't give him more responsibility than he can deal with or get into long discussions about moral issues. If he is four, treat him like someone capable of doing quite a lot of things for himself. If your child is slow in development, try to treat him as though he is the age which he is behaving developmentally, rather than his chronological age.

2. Remember that you can be firm *and* loving. Consistency and firmness help your child to cope with fears and anxieties as well as with his own tempers and frustrations. Don't make unkind threats that you aren't going to carry out – like a threat

to send him away if he's naughty — that is neither firm nor loving.

3. Try to have as few rules as possible, but stick to those you have so that your child knows where he is and what you think is really important. If you keep on at him about trivial things he will never know what is important.

4. Remember that all children go through times of difficulty over eating, tempers, mixing and so on. It doesn't necessarily mean that they are emotionally disturbed, are going to grow up with problems, or that you are a bad parent.

5. Don't expect too much of yourself and feel a failure if you are sometimes irritable or inconsistent. Neither you nor your child have to be perfect. Try not to compare your child to other children. All children are different, and comparisons won't help him to change, but will discourage him and make him angry. Try not to compare yourself to other people either, that's also discouraging, and for all you know, they are secretly wishing they were like you.

6. When your child is going through a difficult stage you naturally become anxious, and your anxiety can lead you to behave in ways which accentuate the difficulty. For instance, some parents try to argue or tease their child out of a problem or play down its importance. But if your child is afraid of the dark or doesn't want to leave you, this is a problem for him which will not just go away. It could help him more to acknowledge that he has a real difficulty and then work out ways of trying to deal with it; for instance, helping your frightened child to say 'I can be brave', 'I can cope with my fear' (see Chapter 8).

7. Try to keep things in perspective, and if a problem is getting you down or you feel at the end of your tether, talk it over with someone sympathetic. They can help you to see that your problems are similar to those of many other parents and children and that there are probably ways of easing the situation.

8. Playfulness is a great help for getting through difficult times, and if your child sees you approaching problems with a sense of humour, it helps him to learn about making the best of a situation.

Jim, aged three and a half ceremoniously made a parcel of his father's hat as a 'present' for himself, while at the same time he was packing up a real present for a friend's birthday party. In this way he coped with his envy in a rather jokey way, instead of having a temper or becoming irritable or demanding.

Children vary in their sense of humour but most of them have an enormous capacity for fun. They delight in games like peek-a-boo and waving goodbye even in the first year, and in the second year like to tease you by offering things and then taking them away. As soon as language develops they begin to develop their imaginary games and fantasies and to play with words.

There are bound to be times when laughing with your toddler is the last thing you feel like doing, but if you can both see the amusing side of a tense situation it will suddenly seem less upsetting and serious. Enjoy your child and have fun.

We know it's not as easy as it sounds to cope with young children; we hope that you will find the ideas in this book helpful.

References

Chapter 1

1. **MacFarlane, J. W., Allen, L., and Honzik, P.** (1954) *A developmental study of behaviour problems of normal children between 21 months and 14 years.* Berkeley and Los Angeles, University of California Press.
2. **Richman, N., Stevenson, J., and Graham, P.** (1975) 'Prevalence of behaviour problems in 3-year-old children: an epidemiological study in a London borough'. *J. Child Psychol. Psychiat. 16*, 277–87.
3. **Thomas, A., Chess, S., and Birch, H. G.** (1968) *Temperament and behaviour disorders in children.* New York, N.Y. University Press.

Chapter 2

1. **Richman, N.** (1977) 'Behaviour problems in preschool children: Family and social factors'. *Brit. J. Psychiat. 131*, 523–7.
2. **Brown, G., and Harris, T.** (1978) *The social origins of depression.* London: Tavistock.
3. **Richman, N.** (1974) 'The effect of housing on preschool children and their mothers'. *Dev. Med. Child Neurol. 16*, 53–6.
4. **Yudkin, S., and Holme, A.** (1969) *Working mothers and their children.* London: Michael Joseph.
5. **Hoffman, L.** (1974) 'The effects of maternal employment on the child – a review of the research'. *Dev. Psychol. 10*, 204–28.
6. **Wallston, B.** (1973) 'The effects of maternal employment on children'. *J. Child Psychol, Psychiat. 14*, 81–96.
7. **Parke, R. D.** (1980) *Fathering.* Fontana: Glasgow.
8. **Beail, N., McGuire, J.** (eds.) (1982) *Fathers. Psychological perspectives.* London: Junction Books.

9. **Moss, P.,** and **Fonda, N.** (eds.) (1980) *Work and the family*. London: Temple Smith.

Chapter 3

1. **Forehand, R.,** and **Peed, S.** (1979) 'Training parents to modify non-compliant behaviour of their children. In A. J. Finch and P. C. Kendall (eds.), *Treatment and research in child psychopathology*. N.Y.: Spectrum.
2. **Forehand, R.,** and **King, H. E.** (1974) 'Pre-school children's non-compliance: effects of short-term therapy'. *J. Community Psychology, 2*, 42–4.

Chapter 4

1. **Patterson, G. R.,** and **Brodsky, G. A.** (1967) 'Behaviour modification programme for a child with multiple problem behaviour'. *J. Child Psychol. Psychiat. 7*, 277–95.
2. **Hawkins, R. P., Peterson, R. F., Schweid, E.,** and **Bijou, S. W.** (1966) 'Behaviour therapy in the home'. *J. Exptl. Child Psychology, 4*, 99–107.
3. **Livingston, S.** (1970) 'Breath holding spells in children'. *J. Amer. Med. Assoc. 2*, 212.

Chapter 5

1. **Schachar, R., Rutter, M.,** and **Smith, A.** (1981) 'The characteristics of situationally and pervasively hyperactive children: implications for syndrome definition'. *J. Child Psychol. Psychiat. 22*, 375–92.
2. **Richman, N., Stevenson, J.,** and **Graham, P.** (1975) 'Prevalence of behaviour problems in 3 year-old children: an epidemiological study in a London borough. *J. Child Psychol. Psychiat. 16*, 277–87.
3. **Taylor, E.** (1979) 'Annotation: Food Additives, Allergy and Hyperkinesis'. *J. Child Psychol. Psychiat. 20*, 357–64.
4. **Schleifer, M.,** *et al.* (1975) 'Hyperactivity in preschoolers and the effect of methyl-phenidate'. *Am. J. Orthopsychiat. 45*, 38–50.

Chapter 6

1. **Thelen, E.** (1979) 'Rhythmical stereotypes in normal human infants'. *Animal Behaviour*, 27, 699–715.
2. **Boniface, D.** and **Graham, P.** (1979) 'The three year old and his attachment to a special soft object'. *J. Child Psychol. Psychiat.* 20, 217–24.
3. **Passman, R. H.**, and **Halonen, J. S.** (1979) 'A developmental survey of young children's attachments to inanimate objects'. *J. Genet. Psychol. 134*, 165–78.
4. **Ozturk, M.**, and **Ozturk, O. M.** (1977) 'Thumb sucking and falling asleep'. *Brit. J. Med. Psychol. 50*, 95–103.
5. **Curzon, M. E. J.** (1974) 'Dental implications of thumb sucking'. *Pediatrics, 54*, 196–9.
6. **Azrin, N. H.**, **Nunn, R. G.**, and **Frantz-Renshaw, S.** (1980) 'Habit reversal of thumbsucking'. *Behav. Research and Therapy, 18*, 395–9.
7. **Bishop, B. R.**, and **Stumphauzer, J. S.** (1973) 'Behaviour therapy of thumbsucking in children'. *Psycholog. Reports 33*, 939–44.
8. **Kravitz, H.**, and **Boehm, J. J.** (1971) 'Rhythmic habit patterns in infancy: their sequence, age of onset and frequency'. *Child Develop. 42*, 399–413.
9. **Sallustro, F.**, and **Atwell, C. W.** (1978) 'Body rocking, headbanging and head rolling in normal children'. *J. Pediatrics 93*, 704–8.

Chapter 7

1. **Weinraub, M.**, and **Lewis, M.** (1977) 'The determinants of children's responses to separation'. *Monogr. Soc. Res. Child Dev. 42*, No. 172.
2. **Rutter, M.** (1980) 'Maternal deprivation 1972–78. New findings: new concepts: new approaches'. *Child Dev. 50*, 283–305.
3. **Montenegro, H.** (1968) 'Severe separation anxiety in two pre-school children: successfully treated by reciprocal inhibition'. *J. Child Psychol. Psychiat. 9*, 93–103.
4. National Association for the Welfare of Children in

Hospital, 7 Exton Street, London, SE1 (01-261-1738), provide leaflets and books about children in hospital.

5. **Melamed, B. G.** (1977) 'Psychological preparation for hospitalization'. In S. Rachman (ed.), *Contribution to medical psychology, Vol. 1.* Pergamon Press.

6. **Melamed, B. G.,** and **Siegel, L. J.** (1975) 'Reduction of anxiety in children facing hospitalization and surgery by use of filmed modelling'. *J. Consult. Psychology 43,* 511–21.

Chapter 8

1. **Jersild, A. T.,** and **Holmes, F. B.** (1935) *Children's fears.* N.Y.: Teachers College.

2. **Cummings, J. D.** (1944) 'The incidence of emotional symptoms in school-children'. *Brit. J. Educ. Psychol. 14,* 151–61.

3. **Graziano, A. M., DeGiovanni, I. S.,** and **Garcia, K. A.** (1979) 'Behavioural treatment of children's fears: a review'. *Psychological Bull. 86,* 804–30.

4. **Tasto, D. L.** (1969) 'Systematic desensitization, mind relaxation and visual imagery in the counterconditioning of a 4-year-old phobic child'. *Behav. Research and Therapy 7,* 409–11.

5. **Karter, F. H., Karoly, P.,** and **Newman, A.** (1975) 'Reduction of children's fear of the dark by competence-related and situational threat-related verbal cues'. *J. Consult. Clin. Psychology 43,* 251–8.

6. **Graziano, A. M.,** and **Mooney, K. C.** (1980) 'Family self-control instruction for children's night-time fear reduction'. *J. Consult. Clin. Psychology 48,* 206–13.

7. **Kelly, C. K.** (1976) 'Play desensitization of fear of darkness in preschool children'. *Behav. Research and Therapy 14,* 79–81.

8. **Melamed, B. G., Hawes, R. R., Heiby, E.,** and **Glick, J.** (1975) 'The use of filmed modelling to reduce the uncooperative behaviour of children during dental treatment'. *J. Dental. Res. 54,* 797–801.

Chapter 9

1. **Yarrow, M.,** and **Waxler, N.** (1976) 'Dimensions and correlates of prosocial behaviour in young children'. *Child Dev.* 47, 118–25.

2. **Lewis, M.,** and **Rosenblum, L.** (1975) *Peer relations and friendship.* N.Y.: Wiley.

3. **Rubin, Z.** (1980) *Children's friendships.* Glasgow: Fontana.

4. **Hartup, W. W.** (1978) 'Children and their friends'. In H. McGurk (ed.), *Issues in childhood social development.* N.Y.: Plenum.

5. **O'Leary, K. D., O'Leary, S.,** and **Becher, W. C.** (1967) 'Modification of deviant sibling interaction in the home'. *Behav. Research and Therapy* 5, 113–20.

Chapter 10

1. **Dunn, J.,** and **Kendrick, C.** (1982) *Siblings. Love, envy and understanding.* London: Grant McIntyre.

Chapter 11

1. **Roberts, K.,** and **Schoelkopf, J.** (1957) 'Eating, sleeping and elimination practices in a group of 2½ year old children'. *Am. J. Dis. Childh. 82,* 121–52.

2. **Richman, N., Stevenson, J.,** and **Graham, P.** (1975) 'Prevalence of behaviour problems in 3 year old children: an epidemiological study in a London borough'. *J. Child Psychol. Psychiat. 16,* 277–87.

3. **Bernal, J.** (1972) 'Crying during the first 10 days of life and maternal responses'. *Dev. Med. Child Neurol. 14,* 362–72.

4. **Kitzinger, S.** (1979) *The experience of breast feeding.* London: Penguin.

5. **Palmer, S., Thompson, R. J.,** and **Linscheid, R.** (1975) 'Applied behavioural analysis in the treatment of childhood feeding problems'. *Devel. Med. Child Neurol. 17,* 333–9.

6. **Wheeler, M. E.,** and **Hess, K. W.** (1976) 'Treatment of juvenile obesity by successive approximation control of eating'. *J. Behav. Ther. and Expt. Psychiat. 7,* 235–41.

Chapter 12

1. **Kaffman, M.,** and **Elizur, E.** (1977) 'Infants who become enuretics'. *Monogr. Soc. Res. in Child Dev.* 42, Serial No. 170.

2. **Brazelton, T. M.** (1962) 'A child oriented approach to toilet training'. *Pediatrics* 29, 121–8.

3. **Foxx, R. M.,** and **Azrin, N. H.** (1973) 'Dry pants: A rapid method of toilet training children'. *Behav. Research and Therapy* 11, 435–42.

4. **MacKeith, R.** (1973) 'The cause of nocturnal enuresis'. In I. Kolvin, R. MacKeith and S. R. Meadow (eds.), *Bladder control and enuresis. Clinics in Dev. Med. Nos. 48/49,* 173–80. London: SIMP/Heinemann.

5. **Stein, Z.** and **Susser, M.** (1967) 'Social factors in the development of sphincter control'. *Dev. Med. Child Neurol.* 9, 692–706.

6. **Weir, K.** (1982) 'Night and day wetting among a population of three year olds'. *Dev. Med. Child Neurol.* 24, 479–84.

7. **Hallgren, B.** (1957) 'Enuresis: A clinical and genetic study'. *Acta. Psych. Neurol. Scand. Suppl.* 114, 1–159.

8. **Doleys, D. M.** (1977) 'Behavioural treatments for nocturnal enuresis in children: a review of the recent literature'. *Psycholog. Bulletin* 84, 30–54.

9. **Lai, M.,** and **Lindsley, O. R.** (1968) 'Therapy of chronic constipation in a young child by arranging social contingencies'. *Behav. Research and Therapy* 6, 484–5.

10. **Edelman, R. I.** (1971) 'Operant conditioning treatment of encopresis'. *J. Behav. Ther. Exper. Psychol.* 2, 71–3.

Index

FOR THE BEST IN PAPERBACKS, LOOK FOR THE

In every corner of the world, on every subject under the sun, Penguin represents quality and variety – the very best in publishing today.

For complete information about books available from Penguin – including Pelicans, Puffins, Peregrines and Penguin Classics – and how to order them, write to us at the appropriate address below. Please note that for copyright reasons the selection of books varies from country to country.

In the United Kingdom: For a complete list of books available from Penguin in the U.K., please write to *Dept E.P., Penguin Books Ltd, Harmondsworth, Middlesex, UB7 0DA*

In the United States: For a complete list of books available from Penguin in the U.S., please write to *Dept BA, Penguin, 299 Murray Hill Parkway, East Rutherford, New Jersey 07073*

In Canada: For a complete list of books available from Penguin in Canada, please write to *Penguin Books Canada Ltd, 2801 John Street, Markham, Ontario L3R 1B4*

In Australia: For a complete list of books available from Penguin in Australia, please write to the *Marketing Department, Penguin Books Australia Ltd, P.O. Box 257, Ringwood, Victoria 3134*

In New Zealand: For a complete list of books available from Penguin in New Zealand, please write to the *Marketing Department, Penguin Books (NZ) Ltd, Private Bag, Takapuna, Auckland 9*

In India: For a complete list of books available from Penguin, please write to *Penguin Overseas Ltd, 706 Eros Apartments, 56 Nehru Place, New Delhi, 110019*

In Holland: For a complete list of books available from Penguin in Holland, please write to *Penguin Books Nederland B.V., Postbus 195, NL–1380AD Weesp, Netherlands*

In Germany: For a complete list of books available from Penguin, please write to *Penguin Books Ltd, Friedrichstrasse 10 – 12, D–6000 Frankfurt Main 1, Federal Republic of Germany*

In Spain: For a complete list of books available from Penguin in Spain, please write to *Longman Penguin España, Calle San Nicolas 15, E–28013 Madrid, Spain*

MY CHILD WON'T SLEEP

Jo Douglas and Naomi Richman

Bringing up children is not easy.

You are often exhausted, irritable and bewildered by the irrational behaviour of your child despite your best efforts and at a loss to know where to turn for advice.

Written by two childcare experts, *My Child Won't Sleep* offers sensible and well-tested methods of dealing with sleeping problems such as fear of the dark, night waking, nightmares and refusal to go to bed, and discusses fresh and constructive approaches to the successful management of night-time routine.

Soothing, experienced and practical, the two authors demonstrate that there are always practical steps you can take to overcome a problem and that – perhaps best of all – you are not alone.

'A fund of practical advice for parents whose child is wakeful' – *Mother and Baby*

'It is based on exhaustive research, studies and interviews . . . This is the kind of unbossy, informative book that belongs on the kitchen shelf . . . so you can reach for it any time your angel turns noisily devilish'
–*Maternity and Mothercraft*

MY CHILD WON'T EAT

Elisabeth Morse

Most parents at some time feel anxious that their child is not eating properly.

Usually this is no more than a temporary setback, but on some occasions a child's refusal to eat persists. Either way, parents need sympathetic advice to help them overcome the difficulty.

In this practical book Elisabeth Morse gives parents a description of the growth and development of a healthy child to use as a yardstick with which to compare their own. She analyses the cause of many common eating problems and gives helpful hints on how to cope with them, gleaned from doctors, health visitors, teachers and other parents.

Written by a qualified nutritionist, *My Child Won't Eat* will provide parents with the facts, help and comfort that will put their minds at rest and allow them to feed their children with confidence.

Audrey Eyton's F-Plus   Audrey Eyton

'Your short-cut to the most sensational diet of the century' – *Daily Express*

Caring Well for an Older Person   Muir Gray and Heather McKenzie

Wide-ranging and practical, with a list of useful addresses and contacts, this book will prove invaluable for anyone professionally concerned with the elderly or with an elderly relative to care for.

Baby and Child   Penelope Leach

A beautifully illustrated and comprehensive handbook on the first five years of life. 'It stands head and shoulders above anything else available at the moment' – Mary Kenny in the *Spectator*

Woman's Experience of Sex   Sheila Kitzinger

Fully illustrated with photographs and line drawings, this book explores the riches of women's sexuality at every stage of life. 'A book which any mother could confidently pass on to her daughter – and her partner too' – *Sunday Times*

Food Additives   Erik Millstone

Eat, drink and be worried? Erik Millstone's hard-hitting book contains powerful evidence about the massive risks being taken with the health of consumers. It takes the lid off the food we eat and takes the lid off the food industry.

Pregnancy and Diet   Rachel Holme

It *is* possible to eat well and healthily when pregnant while avoiding excessive calories; this book, with suggested foods, a sample diet-plan of menus and advice on nutrition, shows how.

PENGUIN HEALTH

Medicines: A Guide for Everybody   Peter Parish

This sixth edition of a comprehensive survey of all the medicines available over the counter or on prescription offers clear guidance for the ordinary reader as well as invaluable information for those involved in health care.

Pregnancy and Childbirth   Sheila Kitzinger

A complete and up-to-date guide to physical and emotional preparation for pregnancy – a must for all prospective parents.

The Penguin Encyclopaedia of Nutrition   John Yudkin

This book cuts through all the myths about food and diets to present the real facts clearly and simply. 'Everyone should buy one' – *Nutrition News and Notes*

The Parents' A to Z   Penelope Leach

For anyone with a child of 6 months, 6 years or 16 years, this guide to all the little problems involved in their health, growth and happiness will prove reassuring and helpful.

Jane Fonda's Workout Book

Help yourself to better looks, superb fitness and a whole new approach to health and beauty with this world-famous and fully illustrated programme of diet and exercise advice.

Alternative Medicine   Andrew Stanway

Dr Stanway provides an objective and practical guide to thirty-two alternative forms of therapy – from Acupuncture and the Alexander Technique to Macrobiotics and Yoga.

A Complete Guide to Therapy   Joel Kovel

The options open to anyone seeking psychiatric help are both numerous and confusing. Dr Kovel cuts through the many myths and misunderstandings surrounding today's therapy and explores the pros and cons of various types of therapies.

Pregnancy   Dr Jonathan Scher and Carol Dix

Containing the most up-to-date information on pregnancy – the effects of stress, sexual intercourse, drugs, diet, late maternity and genetic disorders – this book is an invaluable and reassuring guide for prospective parents.

Yoga   Ernest Wood

'It has been asked whether in yoga there is something for everybody. The answer is "yes"' – Ernest Wood.

Depression   Ross Mitchell

Depression is one of the most common contemporary problems. But what exactly do we mean by the term? In this invaluable book Ross Mitchell looks at depression as a mood, as an experience, as an attitude to life and as an illness.

Vogue Natural Health and Beauty   Bronwen Meredith

Health foods, yoga, spas, recipes, natural remedies and beauty preparations are all included in this superb, fully illustrated guide and companion to the bestselling *Vogue Body and Beauty Book*.

Care of the Dying   Richard Lamerton

It is never true that 'nothing more can be done' for the dying. This book shows us how to face death without pain, with humanity, with dignity and in peace.